Welcome to

101
Amazing
FACTS
~you need to know~

Why do fish have scales? What are killer plants? How does GPS work? What are constellations? For the answers to these questions and many more, look no further than this new collection of conundrums and curiosities from six subject areas. Covering the environment, technology, science, space, transport and history, each section is packed with amazing facts to satisfy even the hungriest of minds.

101 Amazing FACTS
you need to know

Imagine Publishing Ltd
Richmond House
33 Richmond Hill
Bournemouth
Dorset BH2 6EZ
☎ +44 (0) 1202 586200
Website: www.imagine-publishing.co.uk
Twitter: @Books_Imagine
Facebook: www.facebook.com/ImagineBookazines

Publishing Director
Aaron Asadi

Head of Design
Ross Andrews

Editor in Chief
Jon White

Production Editor
Jasmin Snook

Senior Art Editor
Greg Whitaker

Designer
Alexander Phoenix

Photographer
James Sheppard

Cover images courtesy of
Thinkstock, NASA, Juliet Marine,

Printed by
William Gibbons, 26 Planetary Road, Willenhall, West Midlands, WV13 3XT

Distributed in the UK, Eire & the Rest of the World by:
Marketforce, 5 Churchill Place, Canary Wharf, London, E14 5HU
Tel 0203 148 3300 www.marketforce.co.uk

Distributed in Australia by
Gordon & Gotch Australia Pty Ltd, 26 Rodborough Road, Frenchs Forest, NSW, 2086 Australia
Tel: +61 2 9972 8800 Web: www.gordongotch.com.au

How It Works 101 Amazing Facts You Need To Know Volume 3
© 2016 Imagine Publishing Ltd

ISBN 978 1785 463 778

Part of the

HOW IT WORKS
book series

IMAGINE
PUBLISHING

Contents

Environment

Technology

Science

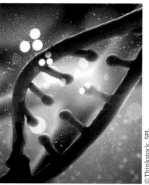

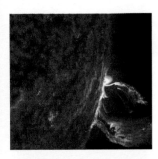

Space

Transport

© NASA

History

Why do fish have scales?

Measuring the threat to Earth's remaining tiger population

Thriving underwater requires some excellent morphological adaptations. One key attribute are scales: strong and durable plates that allow for fluid movement and protection from parasites, scrapes and predators.

There are many types of scale, depending on the fish's evolutionary history. For instance, sharks and rays have placoid scales, while ganoid scales are present on sturgeons and paddlefish. The properties of each scale type are suited to the fish's lifestyle and habitat. The scales all grow in the same direction, tapering towards the tail to make the

≈ *Know your scales* ≈

Get to grips with the different types of fish scales and their uses

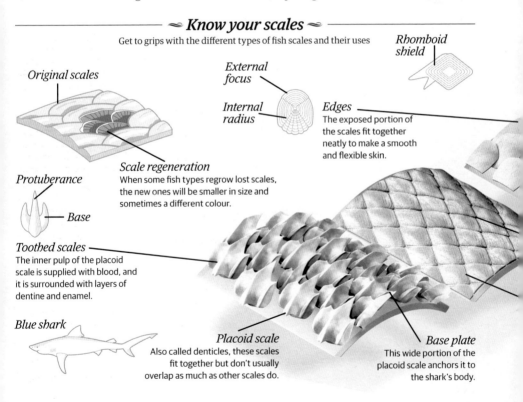

Original scales

External focus

Internal radius

Rhomboid shield

Edges
The exposed portion of the scales fit together neatly to make a smooth and flexible skin.

Scale regeneration
When some fish types regrow lost scales, the new ones will be smaller in size and sometimes a different colour.

Protuberance

Base

Toothed scales
The inner pulp of the placoid scale is supplied with blood, and it is surrounded with layers of dentine and enamel.

Blue shark

Placoid scale
Also called denticles, these scales fit together but don't usually overlap as much as other scales do.

Base plate
This wide portion of the placoid scale anchors it to the shark's body.

fish streamlined. Fish with larger, heavier scales such as the Amazonian arapaima gain more protection but are often more restricted in their movement, whereas species such as eels have much smaller and sometimes microscopic scales that give more flexibility, but at the loss of an armoured exterior.

Scales are either anchored to the body by attaching to bones, or by slotting into envelope-style grooves in the skin. Some scales grow with the fish, meaning they have the same number of scales their whole life, and some types are continually added and/or replaced. Some sport a variety of scale types on their bodies.

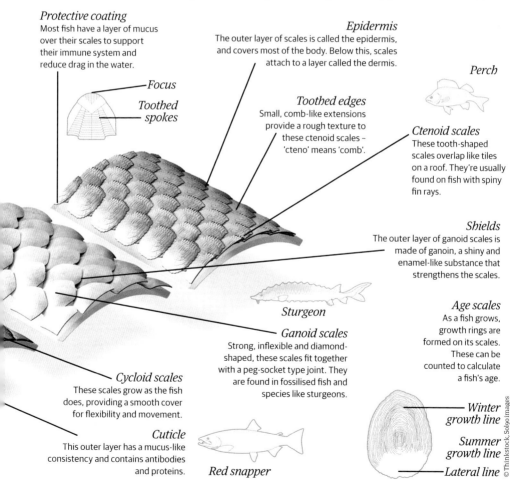

Protective coating
Most fish have a layer of mucus over their scales to support their immune system and reduce drag in the water.

Focus

Toothed spokes

Epidermis
The outer layer of scales is called the epidermis, and covers most of the body. Below this, scales attach to a layer called the dermis.

Perch

Toothed edges
Small, comb-like extensions provide a rough texture to these ctenoid scales – 'cteno' means 'comb'.

Ctenoid scales
These tooth-shaped scales overlap like tiles on a roof. They're usually found on fish with spiny fin rays.

Shields
The outer layer of ganoid scales is made of ganoin, a shiny and enamel-like substance that strengthens the scales.

Sturgeon

Ganoid scales
Strong, inflexible and diamond-shaped, these scales fit together with a peg-socket type joint. They are found in fossilised fish and species like sturgeons.

Age scales
As a fish grows, growth rings are formed on its scales. These can be counted to calculate a fish's age.

Cycloid scales
These scales grow as the fish does, providing a smooth cover for flexibility and movement.

Cuticle
This outer layer has a mucus-like consistency and contains antibodies and proteins.

Red snapper

Winter growth line

Summer growth line

Lateral line

© Thinkstock, Solgo Images

What is the life cycle of a frog?

Discover how a cluster of cells transforms into a hopping, croaking amphibian

Below
Tadpoles are often seen in large groups, that are sometimes called 'clouds'

The cycle begins when frogs come together to mate. The male holds the female in a position known as amplexus and fertilises her eggs as they are laid. A female frog can lay a clutch of around 3,000 to 6,000 eggs.

Within each jelly-like sphere is a black dot - the developing tadpole. The embryos feed off the surrounding jelly as they grow, and then once they have developed rudimentary gills and a tail after about a week or a month (depending on the species), tadpoles hatch. The hatchlings feed on the rest of the frogspawn jelly mass, as well as any algae that has grown on it.

Throughout the next few weeks the tadpoles undergo a fast metamorphosis. First their external gills disappear, replaced by internal gills, which in turn are replaced as lungs develop. The tadpoles also grow legs while they turn into froglets - strange round critters that resemble their adult form, while still retaining their powerful tail. The front legs are the last to develop, and the tadpole's tail is shortened as it is reabsorbed into the body.

The little frog is now a miniature version of its parents at just one centimetre in length. After around 16 weeks of development it can leave the water, breathe air and feed on bugs and insects.

≈ *Underground ant engineering* ≈
Take a peek inside an ant colony

Metamorphosis
In several stages, the tadpole grows adult eyes and front legs and loses its tail.

Amplexus
The male positions himself behind his mate and holds her firmly with his front legs.

Spawning
During spawning the female lays her eggs, which are then fertilised by the male.

Adult frogs
The young frog continues growing once it leaves the water. After around three years it is ready to reproduce.

Eggs
Frogspawn is buoyant, and large clumps of the gelatinous egg mass can normally be seen floating on a pond's surface.

Froglets
As the tadpole grows, it develops a strong tail as well as powerful back legs.

Tadpole
After a few weeks, the small tadpoles hatch with external gills and long tails.

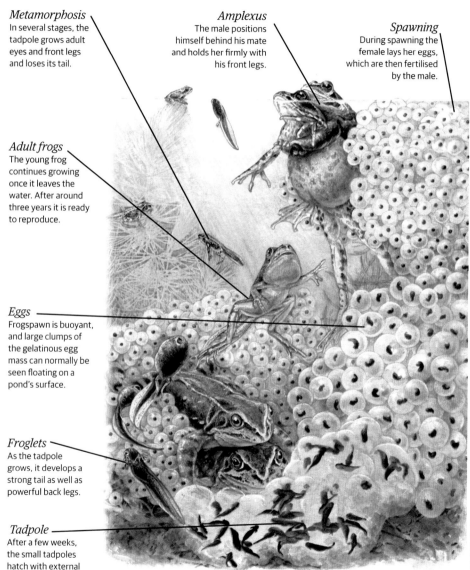

© Thinkstock, Pixabay

How does a venus flytrap work?

Insects don't stand a chance when they land on this killer plant

The carnivorous Venus flytrap sports a menacing-looking mechanism. The spiked, collapsible leaf is laced with drops of sweet nectar to lure in its prey.

When a bug lands, it touches the sensitive trigger hairs on the Venus flytrap's leaves. According to the latest theory, touching one hair does nothing, but touching two causes the trap to snap closed. When the fly struggles, it's likely to trigger three hairs, which readies the plant's cells for digestion, and touching five hairs starts the release of digestive enzymes. The plant can even adjust the amount of digestive fluid produced, depending on how large the prey is.

When an insect lands on the trap and triggers the hairs, this tension is released and the leaves close in a fraction of a second. The large guard hairs fold together, depriving the insect of any means of escape. The digestive fluids break down the soft parts of the prey and absorb the nutrients. Five to 12 days after capture, the trap will reopen to expel the waste exoskeleton.

Marginal spines
These protrusions of the leaf prevent the prey from escaping the trap.

Trigger bristles
When a fly lands, sensitive hairs on the inside of the leaf trigger the trap.

Digestive glands
Spots inside the leaf secrete digestive fluids and absorb nutrients from the prey.

Nectar
The leaves secrete a sweet nectar to lure in its unsuspecting prey, typically insects and spiders.

What are killer plants?

Not satisfied with making food through photosynthesis, these five carnivorous plants capture, kill and eat living prey

Drosera

There are over 100 species of drosera, which are commonly known as 'sundews' as they appear to be constantly covered in dew. These tiny droplets are actually sticky enzymes that trap and start to digest any prey as soon as it lands on the plants' leaves.

Pinguicula

This plant catches prey using sticky leaves. The tacky substance is actually full of digestive enzymes, which break down the insects once they become trapped. When winter arrives, some species of pinguicula become quite dormant and cease their carnivorous activities.

Nepenthes

These plants lure insects, sometimes even rats, into their cup-like pitchers with an attractive scent. Once trapped, the prey drowns in the liquid within the pitcher and is broken down by digestive juices, allowing the plant to absorb the vital nutrients it needs to survive.

Sarracenia

Like Nepenthes, sarracenia is a pitcher plant. Insects are attracted to its colour and sweet scent. As they land at the edge of the pitcher, they often fall in, since the edge is very slippery. Once inside, there is no escape due to the smooth, steep sides of the pitcher.

Venus flytrap

When an insect or arachnid steps on more than one of the tiny hairs of the plant's jaws, it triggers a violent reaction. The hinged mouth snaps down, trapping the prey inside the plant. Digestive enzymes are secreted and it can be several days until the plant re-opens.

What is soil made of?

The ingredients that form one of Earth's most important natural resources

In its simplest form, soil is a gritty mixture of ground-up minerals and decaying organic matter, such as leaf litter from the forest canopy. These raw ingredients are then all completely mixed and churned together by the bugs and worms that live within.

The broken-up rocks that make up soil can come from the bedrock that lies deep below, or from other sources, where rocks, rubble and more soil is transported by forces such as rivers or glaciers.

Below
Soil appears darker when there is more organic matter, or 'humus', present

There are six major types of soil, each with different mineral quantities and qualities. Clay soils are dense but high in nutrients, sandy soils are light, dry and relatively acidic, while silt soils are very fertile and hold plenty of moisture. Loam soils contain a balance of clay, sandy and silt soil types, while peat soil types are full of organic matter and chalky soils contain calcium carbonate and are therefore very alkaline.

Many different types of soil will constantly continue to build up in layers in any given spot over time, making what is known as soil horizons. These layers usually consist of organic matter in various different stages of decay, depending on the locality.

How do Stalagmites and stalactites form?

Discover the development of these curious subterranean spikes

S truggling to tell the difference between these two formations? When you see the letter 'c' in stalactites, think 'ceiling', as they hang from the roofs of caves. And when you see the 'g' in stalagmites, think 'ground', as they rise from the floor like inverted icicles. Both structures are known as speleothems, and are formed over thousands of years, as water trickles through the cave and minerals are deposited layer upon layer.

≈ *Stalactites* ≈

Steady drops of water build these structures downwards

Water drops
Water slowly filters through the many cracks and pores in the rock until it hangs as a drip on the cave ceiling.

Gradual build-up
Calcium carbonate is carried in the water – when it meets the air, it solidifies to form a tiny solid ring around the droplet.

Layer upon layer
Straw stalactites form, where a long and thin deposit is built up with a hollow middle that water drips through.

Sturdier speleothems
As more and more mineral deposits build up on the stalactite, it gets longer, wider and more robust.

≈ *Stalagmites* ≈

Steady drops of water build these structures downwards

Drops from above
As the droplets that also form stalactites hit the floor, calcium carbonate solidifies to form the base.

Rounded shapes
The shape of a stalagmite is a rounded dome. As more drops hit the same patch, the shape builds.

Slower 'growth'
Stalagmites don't build up as quickly as stalactites, but the two structures can eventually form a pillar.

Weather record
Stalagmite layers are compact during wetter years and spaced apart for drier years.

What is Canada's Spotted Lake?

Nestled in a mountainous, forested landscape is a masterpiece of nature

Near the town of Osoyoos, in Canada's British Columbia, lies a lake covered in large, round patches that look as if they have been drawn on by hand. This amazing natural phenomenon appears every summer when scorching temperatures cause the shallow water of the lake to evaporate.

Covering an area of around 16 hectares, the patches that give Spotted Lake its name are actually pools of rich minerals, including calcium, sodium sulphates and magnesium sulphate, as well as traces of silver and titanium. Hues of green and blue decorate the landscape, and throughout the summer the spots change colour and shape as the minerals adapt to further evaporation. When the fresh water disappears, the bed of the lake is exposed, providing natural walkways through the mineral-rich pools.

However, walking through the Spotted Lake pools isn't a possibility for visitors, as it's owned by the Okanagan Nation. To the native community of the Okanagan Valley, the lake is known as 'Kliluk' and holds special spiritual and historical significance. It was bought back from a private owner in 2001 so that it could be protected from development.

Right
There are 365 circles in Spotted Lake, one for every day of the year!

Why are the tropics hotter than the equator?

The sheer power of the wind shapes and sculpts whole landscapes over time

Above
Some of the hottest places on Earth are in subtropical regions, including Death Valley in the US and the Lut desert in Iran

The equator is the latitude that falls at the point on Earth that is an equal distance from the North Pole and the South Pole, making it zero degrees latitude. The tropics surround the equator; the Tropic of Cancer is north of the equator, whereas the Tropic of Capricorn lies to the south. Sunlight hitting the equator generates rising air currents, contributing to cloud cover and thunderstorms which reduce the air temperature by several degrees. At the subtropics, around 20° to 40° above and below the equator, the atmosphere is more stable, so there is little cloud cover. This creates hotter and drier climates than those experienced at the equator.

© Wiki

What is the life cycle of a pine tree?

The sheer power of the wind shapes and sculpts whole landscapes over time

Vast forests of pine trees can be found in many different regions, from the snowy mountains of North America to the open plains of Europe. These hardy evergreen trees can grow in environments that many others can't, favouring acidic or sandy soils and rocky regions at high altitudes.

When exposed to plenty of sunlight, pines can grow up to a towering 80 metres (262 feet) and live for hundreds of years. One bristlecone pine in California is thought to be 5,000 years old, making it one of the oldest trees in the world, but most are cut down long before they reach this ripe old age.

Although pines are native to temperate regions in the Northern Hemisphere, some species have been introduced to southern continents as a valuable source of timber, an industry worth billions of pounds. The young pines that don't go on to become fence panels and furniture usually end up as Christmas trees in homes across the world. Over 77 million pines are planted for this purpose each year, and take six to eight years to reach optimum Christmas tree size. However, when left to their own devices, pine trees grow to have long, slender trunks - almost unrecognisable as the same trees we decorate with tinsel and fairy lights - and use pine cones to reproduce. Each tree uses both male and female structures to create the next generation.

Below
Squirrels help to disperse pine seeds when they bury the cones as a winter food supply

Environment

What is the
life cycle of
a pine tree?

≈ *From cone to tree* ≈

Erosion by the wind helps to hollow out these incredible natural structures

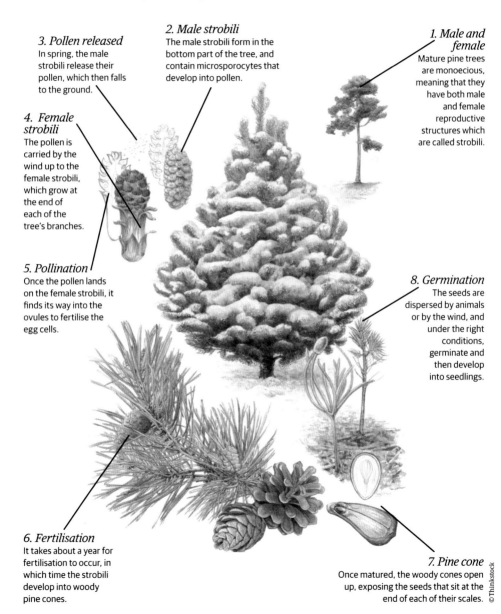

3. Pollen released
In spring, the male strobili release their pollen, which then falls to the ground.

2. Male strobili
The male strobili form in the bottom part of the tree, and contain microsporocytes that develop into pollen.

1. Male and female
Mature pine trees are monoecious, meaning that they have both male and female reproductive structures which are called strobili.

4. Female strobili
The pollen is carried by the wind up to the female strobili, which grow at the end of each of the tree's branches.

5. Pollination
Once the pollen lands on the female strobili, it finds its way into the ovules to fertilise the egg cells.

8. Germination
The seeds are dispersed by animals or by the wind, and under the right conditions, germinate and then develop into seedlings.

6. Fertilisation
It takes about a year for fertilisation to occur, in which time the strobili develop into woody pine cones.

7. Pine cone
Once matured, the woody cones open up, exposing the seeds that sit at the end of each of their scales.

© Thinkstock

Do bumblebees make honey?

Do bumblebees produce honey like their honeybee relatives?

Above
Bumblebees are found to live in small nests, unlike the large, organised hives of their honey-making cousins

The bumblebee is bigger, rounder and fuzzier than the wasp-like honeybee. Both bee types are crucial in the pollination of plants and crops and they both gather nectar to produce honey. However, the substance made by honeybees is produced in large volumes via a rather long-winded method, whereas bumblebees produce a more simplified 'honey' in small quantities. This is actually nectar that the queen bumblebee deposits into wax pots. She uses this to provide food for herself and her young. It is honey in the sense that it's produced by bumblebees from nectar, but it probably won't taste that good on your toast!

What are woodlice?

There's far more to these little critters than meets the eye

Below
Woodlice are so tolerant to heavy metals that they can actually be used as pollution bioindicators

The next time you move something in the garden and see a woodlouse scuttling out from underneath, remember that these little guys are in fact isopod crustaceans! They're more closely related to crabs and lobsters than ants and spiders. Although they're landlubbers, one trait woodlice share with their aquatic cousins is that they use gills to breathe.

They like to live in moist, dark places where there's plenty of decaying material to eat. Their bodies are made up of armoured segments of an exoskeleton that allow them to roll up into balls when threatened (hence the nickname 'pill bug'). As they grow, woodlice need to shed their skin. This happens in two separate stages; the back sheds first, followed by the front, which is why a woodlouse may sport two different colours.

Shuffling on 14 legs, woodlice have two 'uropods' at the back of their bodies. These are for navigation, and some species use them to secrete defensive substances. Uropods are also used for drinking; the louse sucks up water through the tubes into its anus. Any waste is excreted as ammonia gas through pores in the exoskeleton, woodlice don't ever pee!

© Wiki

Do penguins get cold feet?

Discover whether penguin also get frozen feet

Below
Penguins do get cold feet, but are still able to use them

Yes. Penguins do actually get cold get cold feet, however unlike humans, they are still able to continue functioning due to the way their feet are operated. The tendons that are attached to their ankle and toe bones pass through the muscles that are in the warmer parts of their bodies. Though their feet may become cold, the muscles that operate them are still at a normal body temperature. When the external temperature drops significantly, feathers and the fat layer of the body automatically start to protect the feet, which are not allowed to go below freezing. The penguins blood flow also automatically adjusts to ensure that this doesn't happen and the penguin is able to continue functioning.

Why do chickens have combs?

What is that fleshy thing on top of a chickens head?

Chicken combs actually help keep the birds cool. Chickens can't sweat, so when they overheat, blood rushes into the cooler combs on the tops of their heads. Combs are also a good indicator of a chicken's health; a bright red comb is normal, while a pale or darker comb may mean illness. Comb colour, shape and size vary by breed, but males have larger combs than females. They also play a part in mating; a healthy comb is more attractive and signals that a chicken is ready to mate.

Right
This rooster's brilliant red comb keeps him cool and shows that he's fighting fit

How do birds know how to migrate?

How do birds operate natures sat nav?

Some birds migrate more than 70,000 kilometres to escape the cold weather and find more food. Scientists believe there are several methods for migrating. The one most similar to human navigation relies on looking for landscape features, such as coastlines and mountains. A step up from this is to use the position of the Sun and stars, which many birds do. Some are able to use the Earth's magnetic field to migrate, using a part of their brains that acts like an internal compass. Most birds know when to migrate based on the length of the day as well as the temperature. Not all migration is innate, though - some birds have to be taught by their parents or by humans if raised in captivity.

Why is bird poo white?

Why is bird poo so different to other animals?

Most animals make brown poo, but birds are an exception. Instead of having a separate anus for solid waste and a urethra for liquid waste, most birds have a single opening called a cloaca. It's a multipurpose orifice used to excrete waste, lay eggs, and procreate. Birds release urine in the form of uric acid, and it's processed in a way to keep liquid loss to a minimum - hence the white splatter instead of yellow. Often you'll notice a dark blob in the centre; that's the solid waste, or poo.

Why are cats afraid of water?
≋🍃≋

Discover why cats don't like taking a dip

Left
Cats aren't necessarily afraid of water, but don't like how long it takes to get dry

The top layer of cat fur is relatively water resistant, so a light rain shower won't bother it too much. But when a cat gets soaked, its fur tends to become waterlogged. This not only makes the cat sluggish, but it also makes it difficult for the cat to return to a dry, warm state quickly.

However, another theory suggests the so-called fear comes from when owners used to shield their cats from the rain in the earliest periods of domestication.

© Wiki

How do bats sleep upside down without falling?

How do they manage to stay upside down?

Bats' legs are rotated 180 degrees so their knees appear backwards to us, and special tendons in their toes stay flexed so that they don't have to use up any energy to hang on - they only need to let go to fly. In fact, those tendons are so strong that bats continue to hang after they die. As bats are generally very small, hanging upside down doesn't affect their blood flow the way it does ours. They don't get dizzy, and their ability to hang upside down means that bats can roost in places no other animal can.

What is the life cycle of an Oyster?

The bivalve molluscs that seem to have the best of both worlds

Oysters are amazing bivalve molluscs - sea creatures related to slugs and snails that live in hard, hinged shells. Considered a culinary delicacy and aphrodisiac, oysters live naturally in large colonies, called beds or reefs, throughout the world's oceans, as well as being farmed commercially. They feed by filtering plankton from the water column, and are considered to be 'ocean cleaners' due to their ability to filter gallons of water over their gills every day. Capable of living up to 20 years, these critters also have an incredible life cycle.

Oysters take cues from the environment in order to gauge the right time to spawn, but it usually takes place in the spring. When the temperature is at an optimum value (this varies depending on the oyster's specific location), the male oysters release sperm into the water, and the female oysters draw it in. Once their eggs are fertilised, they then release them into the water column to begin their journey.

The fertilised eggs grow as free-swimming larvae until it's time to settle. They then seek out a hard substrate to attach to, keeping them anchored as they mature.

One of the surprising things about oysters is that they are able to spawn as both male and female. All oysters settle and begin adult life as male, then after spawning once they switch sexes and develop as females to spawn again, this time with eggs rather than sperm. This phenomenon can happen twice in one season!

Below
Settled oyster larvae are known as spat, and measure just a few millimetres long

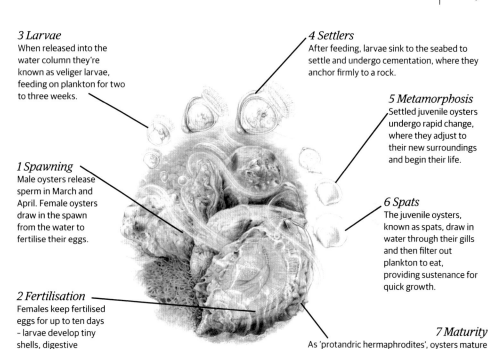

3 Larvae
When released into the
water column they're
known as veliger larvae,
feeding on plankton for two
to three weeks.

4 Settlers
After feeding, larvae sink to the seabed to
settle and undergo cementation, where they
anchor firmly to a rock.

5 Metamorphosis
Settled juvenile oysters
undergo rapid change,
where they adjust to
their new surroundings
and begin their life.

1 Spawning
Male oysters release
sperm in March and
April. Female oysters
draw in the spawn
from the water to
fertilise their eggs.

6 Spats
The juvenile oysters,
known as spats, draw in
water through their gills
and then filter out
plankton to eat,
providing sustenance for
quick growth.

2 Fertilisation
Females keep fertilised
eggs for up to ten days
– larvae develop tiny
shells, digestive
systems and swimming
and feeding organs.

7 Maturity
As 'protandric hermaphrodites', oysters mature
after four years as males, then after spawning
they become female and produce eggs.

Why do oysters make pearls?

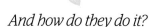

And how do they do it?

An oyster is a mollusc, and therefore has a hard outer wall known as a mantle, which covers and protects certain organs. When an intruder - such as a grain of sand - enters an oyster's shell and lodges itself between the shell and the mantle, it irritates the oyster, causing it to promptly cover the foreign body with a mineral substance that it secretes from its shell, called nacre - also known as mother of pearl. The oyster coats it with more and more nacre until it forms a pearl. The shiny spheres are actually therefore the product of an immune response. Pearl 'farmers' can trigger the response by inserting a grain of sand into the shell.

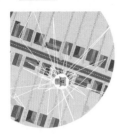

Left
We thought our cat was a lazy old mog, but her GPS tracker shows she is pretty active

How does GPS work?

The hardware that is in the sky explained

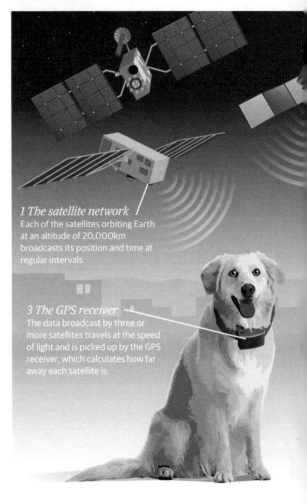

1 The satellite network
Each of the satellites orbiting Earth at an altitude of 20,000km broadcasts its position and time at regular intervals.

3 The GPS receiver
The data broadcast by three or more satellites travels at the speed of light and is picked up by the GPS receiver, which calculates how far away each satellite is.

Right now, there are 31 satellites circling Earth in what is known as the Global Positioning System (GPS) Constellation, feeding back information to millions of GPS devices. Whether you're searching for nearby car parks on your sat nav or tracking down a lost pet, the technology works in the same way.

A GPS receiver in your pet tracker locates at least three of these satellites to calculate exactly where on the planet it is. To do this, the receiver intercepts signals from the satellites and calculates how long it took them to arrive. Because the signals always travel at the speed of light, it is even possible to work out the distances between each of the satellites and your furry friend.

The exact position of the receiver can be pinpointed via a process called trilateration. Say your pet's tracker receives signals from three satellites. It can calculate how far away each satellite is, but not which direction the individual signals came from. For example, if one signal is calculated to come from 20,000 kilometres away, the receiver could lie anywhere on an imaginary sphere with a 20,000-kilometre

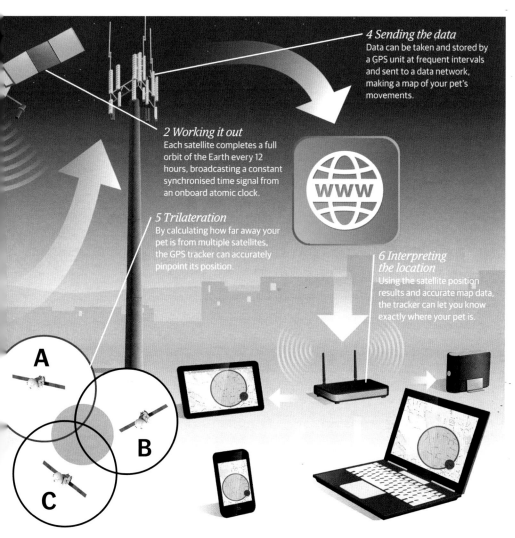

4 Sending the data
Data can be taken and stored by
a GPS unit at frequent intervals
and sent to a data network,
making a map of your pet's
movements.

2 Working it out
Each satellite completes a full
orbit of the Earth every 12
hours, broadcasting a constant
synchronised time signal from
an onboard atomic clock.

5 Trilateration
By calculating how far away your
pet is from multiple satellites,
the GPS tracker can accurately
pinpoint its position.

**6 Interpreting
the location**
Using the satellite position
results and accurate map data,
the tracker can let you know
exactly where your pet is.

A

B

C

radius surrounding that particular satellite.
This is actually why multiple satellites
are required in GPS; finding where three
or more of these spheres from different
satellites intersect enables the receiver to
figure out exactly where your pet is. The
more satellite signals the tracker is able to
pick up, the more accurate the ultimate
position will be.

As tech become more complex, GPS
receivers are able to store more detailed
maps. So, if your pet is wearing a tracking
device, you will be able to locate specific
streets, fields or buildings that it walks past.

What is a cyborg plant?

Discover how to turn a living rose into an electric circuit

If you struggle to keep your houseplants alive, then the idea of a shrub that can alert you when it needs watering would certainly be appealing. Thanks to researchers in Sweden, that idea is much closer to becoming reality.

The team from Linköping University has created the very first electronic plant, which they say opens up the possibility of being able to read and regulate plant growth by measuring the concentration of their various molecules, as well as making use of the energy they produce through photosynthesis in a fuel cell.

To create their cyborg rose bush, the researchers used a synthetic polymer called PEDOT-S, which was drawn up through the plant's stem by capillary action - the same process plants use to absorb water. Once inside this channel, the polymer converted itself into a thin film that could conduct electrical signals, but still left enough room for water and nutrients to pass through and keep the plant alive. By placing an electrode at each end of the conductive film, the team was then able to create a transistor: an electronic switch that completed the circuit.

Below
The researchers have been able to create electrochemical cells in plants, which can change the colour of the leaves

How do seabed mining robots work?

The deep-sea machines that extract valuable minerals from the ocean floor

Below
Computers contain fans and heatsinks to remove excess heat and keep them cool

Spewing hot, chemical-rich fluids from beneath the seafloor, hydrothermal vents are a valuable source of minerals, including copper, nickel, silver and gold. However, as they lie hundreds of metres below the ocean surface, getting at these sought-after deposits is a tricky business. This is why Toronto-based mining company Nautilus Minerals is planning to deploy a team of robots, or Seafloor Production Tools, to do all the hard work for them.

First, the Auxiliary Cutter will carve benches into the seafloor's rough terrain so the other machines have a flat area to work on. The Bulk Cutter will then slice away material from the seabed using spiked rotating drums, leaving it for a Collecting Machine to draw in as seawater slurry. This machine will push the slurry of crushed rock and water through a pipe to the Riser and Lifting System, which will then pump it up to a Production Support Vessel on the surface. Here, the slurry will be filtered to extract the minerals, and the leftover seawater will be pumped back to the seafloor.

How do Pinball machines work?

How the ball gets rolling on this arcade classic

Metal rod
Players can attempt to move the ball by shaking the machine. The tilt mechanism keeps them from going overboard.

Conductive ring
Too much movement causes the bob to move and touch the conductive ring to the metal rod, completing a circuit.

Pendulum bob
If the bob touches the ring, the machine shuts down, forcing the ball down the drain and forfeiting earned points.

Plunger
Pulling on the spring-loaded plunger launches the ball into the playfield.

Flippers
Flippers are electromechanically controlled levers. Pressing the buttons completes a circuit, pushing the flipper up or down.

Ball
Pinball machines usually use either steel or chrome balls, although some even use ceramic.

Ramp
This inclined plane sets the ball off on its first trajectory.

Today's pinball machines are much flashier and more sophisticated than their ancestors, but they all retain the same basics of gameplay. The object of the game is to keep the ball from going down the drain, while scoring as many points as possible.

To launch the ball into the playfield, the player pulls back a spring-loaded plunger and releases. The tension of the spring can be manipulated based on how much the plunger is pulled, which is useful for aiming at specific targets. The playfield comprises one or more sets of flippers on each side, the only part of the game that the player can control once the ball is launched.

Numerous other features that can affect the ball include kickers, slingshots, switches, spinners, bumpers, ramps, and targets. The backbox, or back glass, contains all of the machine's electronics and is covered with decorative art. The player must carefully time when they move the flippers, sending the ball in the desired direction and ultimately stopping it from falling out of the playfield.

What is inside a loud speaker?

Learn how speakers make noise

Below
All speakers great and small use electromagnet mechanisms to pump out the sound waves

In their simplest form, speakers use an electromagnet to move a cone-shaped membrane that vibrates to make noise. Inside the speaker, the mobile electromagnet is placed in front of a fixed, normal magnet. As electricity passes through the coil of the electromagnet, the direction of the magnetic field rapidly changes. This causes the electromagnet to continually be repelled by and attracted to the normal magnet, moving the cone-shaped membrane back and forth. The membrane pushes and pulls the surrounding air molecules, creating waves of sound that reach your ears.

The pitch of the sound is governed by the frequency of the vibrations, while the volume is controlled by the amplitude, or height, of the sound waves. Some types of speakers use multiple cones of various sizes to replicate the different frequencies in a piece of music.

～ Inside a Harman speaker ～

The key components that allow you to listen to music loud and clear

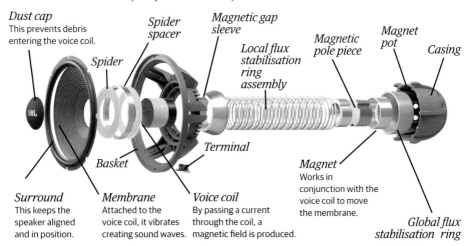

Dust cap
This prevents debris entering the voice coil.

Spider spacer

Magnetic gap sleeve

Local flux stabilisation ring assembly

Magnetic pole piece

Magnet pot

Casing

Spider

Terminal

Magnet
Works in conjunction with the voice coil to move the membrane.

Basket

Surround
This keeps the speaker aligned and in position.

Membrane
Attached to the voice coil, it vibrates creating sound waves.

Voice coil
By passing a current through the coil, a magnetic field is produced.

Global flux stabilisation ring

How does surround sound work?

Discover the science behind this clever technology

Below
Surround sound can improve the home cinema experience

There are various different surround sound systems, but they all rely on having a number of speakers surrounding the listener. For example, in a 5.1 surround sound system commonly found in home cinema, there is a centre speaker, including a subwoofer for bass, two stereo speakers in front and another pair of surround sound speakers behind the listener. A film soundtrack has components for each speaker encoded, so when it is played, the various sounds come from different parts of the room. The trick to make it seem like someone is walking up behind you is simply to play the sound from the speaker in that direction.

© Thinkstock

What are noise-cancelling headphones?

How does this audio technology use speakers to reduce ambient sound?

Below
Active noise-cancelling headphones can block out up to 70 per cent of background noise

Noise-cancelling headphones can reduce ambient sound around you. Active noise-cancelling headphones use special materials, but go one step further and create their own sound waves too. Inside the earpiece is a small microphone that detects ambient sound and feeds it to a digital processor, which analyses the sound wave's composition. It then creates a sound wave opposite of the one it analysed. This 'anti-sound' wave has the same sized peaks and troughs as the background noise, but they are inverted.

These anti-sound waves are then played back from a small speaker in the ear cup, actively blocking the ambient sound waves through a phenomenon known as destructive interference. When the incoming sound wave is at a peak, the anti-sound wave is at a trough, and the sum of these two waves adds to zero, resulting in minimal external sound.

© Thinkstock

≈ *Active noise-cancelling* ≈

How does the system hear, analyse and block unwanted sound?

Speaker
The speaker receives the newly created sound waves and plays them into the ear cup.

Ambient sound waves
The height of a sound wave's peaks indicate its volume, while the frequency determines the pitch.

New sound waves
The peaks and troughs of the anti-sound waves are the inverted versions of those of the ambient sound.

Noise-cancelling circuitry
This circuitry analyses the ambient noise and uses this information to create a sound wave that will counteract it.

Cancelling sound
The new sound waves are 180 degrees out of phase with unwanted noise, cancelling it out by producing an 'opposite' sound.

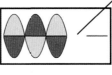

Microphone
Mounted within the ear cup, it 'listens' to external sound waves.

How do multicopters take off?

The science and tech that gets commercial drones into the air

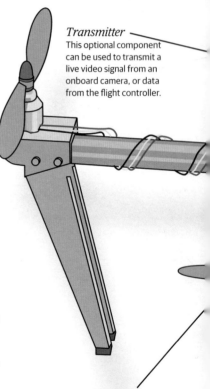

Transmitter
This optional component can be used to transmit a live video signal from an onboard camera, or data from the flight controller.

Drones come in all shapes and sizes, from the mammoth machines used by the military, to the toys you fly in your back garden. However, while they are all operated remotely, the methods they use to get into the air can differ greatly.

Those that take off like normal airplanes use engines or vertical propellers to create thrust, propelling them forwards and causing air to flow rapidly over the wings. The curved shape of the wings then deflect air, creating a difference in pressure above and below. As the air pressure below the wing is higher, this generates lift to push the drone upwards.

VTOL (Vertical Take Off and Landing) drones however, don't need a runway for take-off. They use engines or horizontal propellers to direct thrust downwards, thereby creating lift that gets them off the ground. This is the method favoured by commercial drones, which often come in the form of multicopters.

These miniature flying machines feature four or more horizontal propellers, which create plenty of thrust to allow them to hover above the ground. The propellers rotate in opposing directions to avoid spinning the multicopter out of control. They can also be used to change its direction by increasing or decreasing the speed at which certain propellers rotate.

Electronic speed control
The ESC takes power from the battery and sends it to the motors according to the flight controller's instructions.

≈ *The anatomy of a drone* ≈

Explore the components that make multicopter flight possible

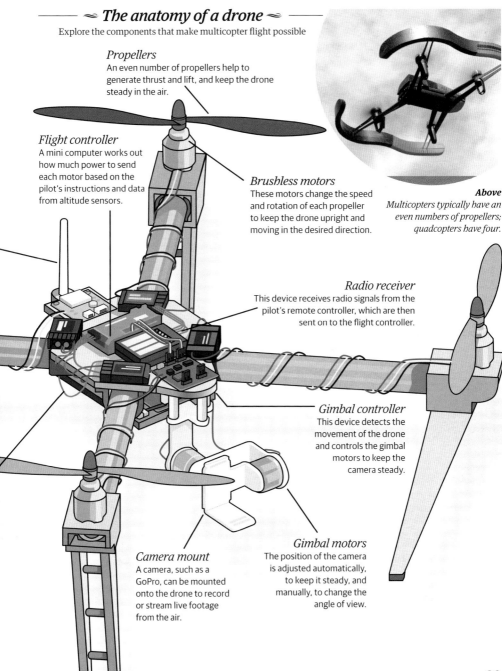

Propellers
An even number of propellers help to generate thrust and lift, and keep the drone steady in the air.

Flight controller
A mini computer works out how much power to send each motor based on the pilot's instructions and data from altitude sensors.

Brushless motors
These motors change the speed and rotation of each propeller to keep the drone upright and moving in the desired direction.

Above
Multicopters typically have an even numbers of propellers; quadcopters have four.

Radio receiver
This device receives radio signals from the pilot's remote controller, which are then sent on to the flight controller.

Gimbal controller
This device detects the movement of the drone and controls the gimbal motors to keep the camera steady.

Camera mount
A camera, such as a GoPro, can be mounted onto the drone to record or stream live footage from the air.

Gimbal motors
The position of the camera is adjusted automatically, to keep it steady, and manually, to change the angle of view.

What is drone racing?

The new high-octane sport putting quadcopter pilots to the test

Swooping through the air at 130 kilometres per hour, flying through narrow hallways and veering around tight corners, this isn't your average quadcopter flight. In the world of professional drone racing, pilots' skills are always pushed to the limits as they manoeuvre their flying machines around some of the toughest obstacle courses on Earth.

Below
All DRL pilots have a fleet of DRL Racer 2 drones to use for each race

One of the biggest tournaments of this kind is the Drone Racing League (DRL), a global competition that sees the world's top drone pilots compete for prize money and, more importantly, world champion status. This is essentially a Formula 1 competition for drones and it features a series of races held in enormous sports stadiums and derelict buildings around the world. All of the competing pilots fly the same model of drone, the DRL Racer 2, in order to test their skills on a level playing field. In each race, they score points by passing checkpoints and finishing the course within the allotted time, and at the end of the heats the pilot with the most points is crowned the winner.

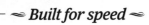

∞ *Built for speed* ∞

The custom-made DRL Racer 2 drone is piloted using a remote control, which sends signals to the craft via radio link. DRL's patented new radio technology ensures reception is never lost, even when the drone flies out of sight through hallways and underground, so the pilot is always in control. HD cameras mounted on the drone transmit a live video feed, also via radio link, to goggles worn by the pilot, enabling them to get a drone's-eye view of the course as if they were in the cockpit.

The drones themselves are made from lightweight carbon fibre, so they only weigh around 800 grams, and can reach top speeds of 130 kilometres per hour. 100 colour LEDs make each quadcopter easily identifiable and are bright enough for the audience to see the action from hundreds of metres away. After every lap, each pilot's drone is replaced with a new fully-charged model, ensuring they can go the distance.

≈ *The Gates of Hell* ≈
This abandoned power plant is the ultimate drone obstacle course

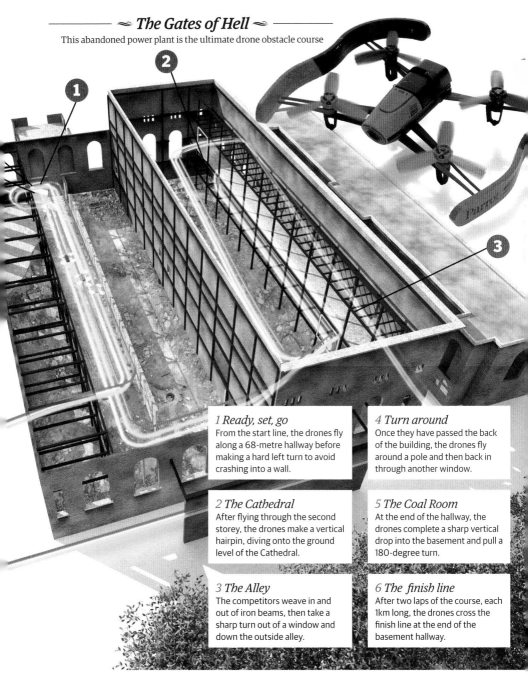

1 Ready, set, go
From the start line, the drones fly along a 68-metre hallway before making a hard left turn to avoid crashing into a wall.

2 The Cathedral
After flying through the second storey, the drones make a vertical hairpin, diving onto the ground level of the Cathedral.

3 The Alley
The competitors weave in and out of iron beams, then take a sharp turn out of a window and down the outside alley.

4 Turn around
Once they have passed the back of the building, the drones fly around a pole and then back in through another window.

5 The Coal Room
At the end of the hallway, the drones complete a sharp vertical drop into the basement and pull a 180-degree turn.

6 The finish line
After two laps of the course, each 1km long, the drones cross the finish line at the end of the basement hallway.

Why do computers get hot as you use them?

Learn why our devices start to overheat with use

Above
Computers contain fans and heatsinks to remove excess heat and keep them cool

All of the electronic components inside your computer have electrical resistance. This means that some of the electric energy that flows through the computer gets dissipated as heat energy as current passes through the electronics, just like the heating element in an electric fire or cooker. Moving parts and motors, such as discs spinning inside hard drives, can also generate heat. The faster your computer is running then the hotter it will get. However, high temperatures can damage the sensitive electronics in computers, so the heat has to be removed somehow. Even though most desktop and laptop computers have fans and heatsinks to keep the electronics cool, the processor can be hot enough to fry an egg.

How does temperature affect battery power?

*What is actually happening when
your battery heats up?*

Below
*Batteries work better in
warmer temperatures, as
heat aids the chemical
reaction inside*

Computers work better when they're cooler, so you'd expect the same to be true for batteries, right? Wrong. The current inside a traditional battery is produced by a chemical reaction that generates electrons. The warmer it is, the more vigorous that reaction - and vice versa when it's cold. That's why car batteries tend to fail in winter, and why you might be able to coax them back into life by heating them up. However, there's a sting in the tail here.

Batteries certainly generate more power when they're warm, but they also have a shorter lifespan - partly because of the extra power, and partly because of the risk of damage to individual cells from overheating. For lead-acid batteries is that increasing the temperature by eight degrees Celsius cuts the battery's life in half.

Are electronics designed to break?

Are our devices programmed to fail after a certain amount of time?

Above
The policy of designing products to break easily is called planned obsolescence

Many devices are only designed to have a short life. In some cases it's because designing them to last longer would make them expensive, yet often it's deliberate. Manufacturers use materials they know will wear out or break easily, make maintenance difficult, or design circuits to get gradually degraded by too much heat. Ideally, this leads to products failing just after the warranty runs out.

What are the metals in your phone?

Discover the hidden treasure inside your handheld device

The average smartphone contains up to 62 different metals, some of which are rare and valuable. As much as 15 per cent of the phone's weight is accounted for by copper, which is used to make the tracks that conduct electricity between components. Copper is used because it has low resistance and is fairly soft.

Gold is nearly 600 times more expensive than copper but has slightly higher resistance. It is still favoured for certain connections on a phone circuit board because it doesn't corrode. It's harder to solder, because it dissolves into the normal tin-silver-copper solder alloy used in the electronics industry. Gold contacts need to be attached using special indium-tin solders or bonded directly using both heat and ultrasound energy.

A typical smartphone only contains about 40 milligrams of the metal tantalum but it is crucial to the miniaturisation of mobile phone technology. Used to make powerful capacitors, which store electricity and are a fraction of the size of ordinary electrolytic capacitors.

∾ *Mobile metal map* ∾

Why does your phone need so many different kinds of metal?

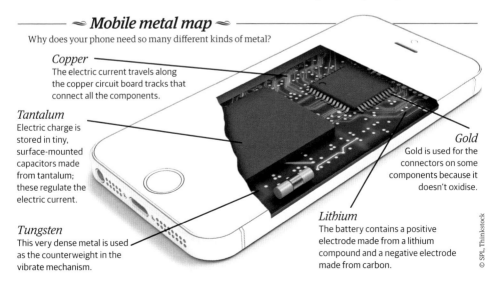

Copper
The electric current travels along the copper circuit board tracks that connect all the components.

Tantalum
Electric charge is stored in tiny, surface-mounted capacitors made from tantalum; these regulate the electric current.

Tungsten
This very dense metal is used as the counterweight in the vibrate mechanism.

Gold
Gold is used for the connectors on some components because it doesn't oxidise.

Lithium
The battery contains a positive electrode made from a lithium compound and a negative electrode made from carbon.

© SPL, Thinkstock

How do computers detect robots?

Bot spotting is an arms race between websites and spammers

When you register at a new website, the line of wavy or distorted text that you have to type in is called a CAPTCHA. This stands for Completely Automated Public Turing test to tell Computers and Humans Apart.

Originally reading text against a busy background was hard for bots. But now the best bots can now read CAPTCHAs with 99.8 per cent accuracy, better than humans!

Some even ask you to click the images of dogs in a grid of images, or identify whether a basketball, rugby ball or ice cream should go with the picture of a basketball hoop.

Right
*Distorted text is
designed to catch
robot spammers*

© Thinkstock

What happens inside a smoke detector?

Annoying when toast burns, but these ear-piercing devices save lives

Below
*Detectors are placed
high up because hot
smoke is less dense
than air, so it rises*

There are two main types of smoke detector: optical and ionisation. Optical detectors contain an infrared light beam pointing toward a photocell, generating electricity when light falls on it. When there is no smoke, the light reaches the photocell unobstructed. When smoke enters the detector and blocks the beam of light, so the photocell can no longer produce an electric current, triggering the alarm and alerting people to danger.

Ionisation detectors contain a radioactive substance. This element constantly emits alpha particles, which pass between two charged metal plates called electrodes. The alpha particles collide with air molecules and split into positive ions and negative electrons. Charged particles are attracted to opposite electrodes, causing a current to flow. Smoke particles attach to ions, neutralising them. A sensor detects the drop in current and the alarm is triggered.

What are rubbish islands?

Building houses on floating plastic bottles is the ultimate in eco-living

Joyxee Island floats just off the coast of Mexico on top of approximately 100,000 plastic bottles. As the bottles are sealed and kept in darkness beneath the island, they don't deteriorate in the Sun's ultraviolet rays, and the roots of mangroves planted above help to hold them all in place. The island is 25 metres in diameter and strong enough to support a two-storey home, complete with a solar-powered waterfall and a wave-powered washing machine. The island is anchored in place by wooden posts driven into the seabed, and is also tethered to the coast by a long rope.

How to make a floating island

A step-by-step to creating your very own eco-paradise

1 Gather the bottles
Tightly seal 100,000 empty plastic bottles destined for landfill or recycling.

2 Tie them together
Place the bottles inside strong nets and then tie them all together to create one large floating structure.

3 Lay down some roots
Secure pallets of plywood and bamboo on top and cover them with sand and soil. Plant mangroves so that the roots will help hold the whole structure together.

Land reclamation success stories

New York
Manhattan Island used to be a thin crop of marshland, but since 1609 it has expanded. The southwest tip was once part of the Hudson River.

Sydney Olympic Park
The area on which the 2000 Summer Olympics were held was originally wetland, and it cost over $100 million to decontaminate it.

Netherlands
Vast areas of the Netherlands have been reclaimed from lakes and the North Sea. Today, about 27 per cent of the Netherlands is below sea level.

© Thinkstock, Wiki

Do we know the science behind a BBQ?

It takes physics, chemistry and biology to grill a perfect burger

Whether your barbecue is plumbed into a gas tank, or is a more traditional coal or wood-fired burner, there are two key ingredients for a good grilling: heat and smoke. Barbecuing is very different from cooking on a hob or in an oven. On the hob, the heat moves from ring to pan to meat mainly by conduction. The metal pan is in physical contact with the heat source, and the meat is in direct contact with the pan. Alternatively, when meat is cooked in an oven, heat mainly travels by convection. The element heats the air, which circulates around the oven, and around your food.

Below
Drips of fat create little flames, releasing flavour molecules into the air

On a barbecue, however, the burgers and sausages are far above the coals, and with the lid off, convection isn't nearly as important as it is in the oven. Instead, most of the heat comes from infrared radiation. Radiant heat is absorbed by dark surfaces, so lining your barbecue with shiny foil can help to direct all of the warmth to where you need it. When using coals, waiting long enough for them to turn white with ash ensures that they are evenly heated through.

As the meat dries out on the outer edges, it starts to brown; sugar reacts with protein to create that distinctive barbecued crust. You can do this indoors on the hob too, but to get that authentic barbecue taste, you need smoke.

When fats and juices drip down on to the barbecue, they burn, releasing flavour and odour molecules that rise up, filling the air with the scent of summer, and sticking to the surface of the meat.

© Dreamstime

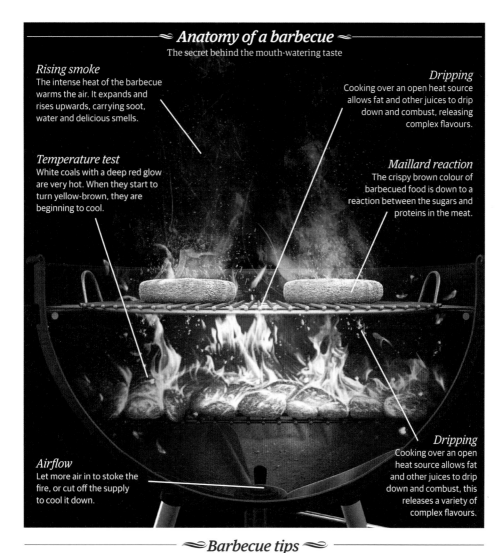

≈ Anatomy of a barbecue ≈
The secret behind the mouth-watering taste

Rising smoke
The intense heat of the barbecue warms the air. It expands and rises upwards, carrying soot, water and delicious smells.

Dripping
Cooking over an open heat source allows fat and other juices to drip down and combust, releasing complex flavours.

Temperature test
White coals with a deep red glow are very hot. When they start to turn yellow-brown, they are beginning to cool.

Maillard reaction
The crispy brown colour of barbecued food is down to a reaction between the sugars and proteins in the meat.

Dripping
Cooking over an open heat source allows fat and other juices to drip down and combust, this releases a variety of complex flavours.

Airflow
Let more air in to stoke the fire, or cut off the supply to cool it down.

≈ Barbecue tips ≈

1 Wait for the coals to go white
Not only does this mean they are hot enough, the coating of ash will help to control the amount of heat they radiate.

2 Preheat the grill
If you're after those charred grill lines, you need to make sure that your grill is scorching before you put your burgers on.

3 Don't bother searing
This technique is quite often thought to seal in the meat's juices, but it may actually do the opposite.

4 Turn frequently
No one likes a burnt sausage. Make sure you keep them moving to prevent one side heating up too much.

5 Let it rest
By doing this, you are allowing the muscle fibres to relax a little, so they hold on to more water when the meat is cut.

Why does coffee spill?

Why is it so hard to carry a cup of coffee?

Above
Researchers advise walking slowly and not filling the cup to the top

© Dreamstime

R esearchers at the University of California, Santa Barbara, carried out a study in which they recorded volunteers as they carried coffee cups to expose the secret behind the spill. What they found was that it's all down to a combination of cup size, coffee fluid dynamics, and the way we walk.

Fluid sloshing inside a container tends towards a natural frequency, a bit like a liquid pendulum. This varies with the size of the cup and the properties of the liquid, but for coffee in a regular mug, the natural frequency is close to walking rhythm. As you walk along, the liquid starts to sway and little irregularities in your step amplify the effect. The faster you accelerate, the more likely you are to spill.

Putting a lid on your cup can actually make things a whole lot worse. As the coffee sloshes, some creeps along the underside of the lid, and climbs up the side of the cup. When these two streams collide, they shoot out of the drinking hole, creating a coffee volcano.

Why do teapots drip?

What causes your favourite beverage to drip out of the spout?

Fluid dynamics researchers at the University of Lyon in France have been hard at work finding out why teapot spouts are so prone to dripping. They found that these post-pour spillages are down to the 'hydro-capillary' effect; as you pour the tea, some of the liquid tracks down the outside of the spout. This is influenced by the shape of the spout, how fast the tea is poured, and how water-repellent the teapot is. Metal teapots with straight-edged spouts are much less prone to dripping than their curvy porcelain counterparts.

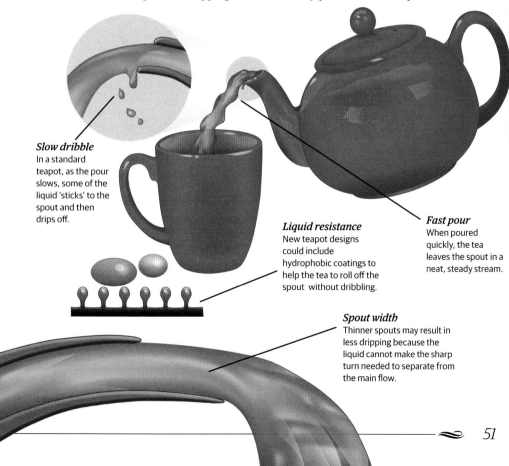

Slow dribble
In a standard teapot, as the pour slows, some of the liquid 'sticks' to the spout and then drips off.

Liquid resistance
New teapot designs could include hydrophobic coatings to help the tea to roll off the spout without dribbling.

Fast pour
When poured quickly, the tea leaves the spout in a neat, steady stream.

Spout width
Thinner spouts may result in less dripping because the liquid cannot make the sharp turn needed to separate from the main flow.

Is the five-second rule real?

Is there any logic behind it?

Below
Whether dropped food is safe to eat depends on the type and number of pathogens present on the floor

Every schoolchild has heard that if you pick food up within five seconds of dropping it, it's safe to eat, but is this an urban myth? To test the idea, researchers at the Aston University in the UK dropped toast, pasta, biscuits and sweets onto a variety of different floor surfaces, and tested them for the presence of common bacteria at time points between three and 30 seconds. Bacteria do transfer before the magic five seconds is up, but generally the food is still edible. Dropping food onto carpet was better than flinging it at a hard, flat surface like laminate, and dry food fared better than wet.

Why does toast burn?

What is it that makes toast smell and taste so good?

Below

Toast can go from white to charred in just a few seconds

Bread in its simplest form is made from wheat flour, yeast and water. The flour contains carbohydrates and proteins, and these are the key ingredients of a chemical reaction known as the Maillard reaction.

Above around 140 degrees Celsius, the chemical groups called aldehydes in bread start to react with the amino groups found in the wheat proteins.

The rate at which your bread turns to toast, and then to charcoal, depends on its composition, and various sugars and amino acids produce different flavour and odour molecules when they undergo the Maillard reaction. In general, the drier the slice, the faster these reactions occur, and the quicker the toast will burn.

≈ *The taste of toast* ≈

Complex chemicals are responsible for the distinctive smell and taste of toast

1 Bread

Bread contains proteins (made of amino acids) and carbohydrates (sugars).

2 Heat

At temperatures above 140˚C, amino acids and sugars start to combine.

3 Sugar

The sugars found in bread include glucose, fructose, maltose and also lactose.

4 Amino acids

There are 20 amino acids, each with a slightly different structure.

5 Glycosylamine

Sugars and amino acids combine to form unstable compounds called glycosylamines.

6 Ketosamine

Glycosylamines are rearranged to form ketosamines, or Amadori compounds.

Step 1

During the first stage of the Maillard reaction, a sugar and an amino acid combine.

③ Sugar (glucose) ④ Amino group ⑤ Glycosylamine (+ water)

Step 2

The structure made in step one undergoes rearrangement, forming an Amadori compound.

1, 2-Enaminol ⑥ Amadori compound

Step 3 ⑦

The compound made in step two can undergo further reactions, producing a range of different molecules.

Reductions

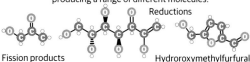

Fission products Hydroroxymethylfurfural

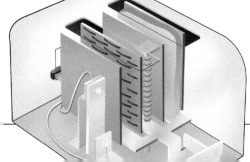

What is Junk DNA?

≈ ⚛ ≈

Why is there so much rubbish in the human genome?

≈ **What is DNA?** ≈
The complex molecule that carries
your genetic information

Chromosome
Chromosomes in the
nucleus of most cells
consist of long strands
of deoxyribonucleic
acid, or DNA.

L ess than two per cent of the three billion 'letters' of the human genome contains proper genes. That leaves an overwhelming majority of our DNA code that has no obvious function - so why does it exist?

Most of the human genome is dull and repetitive, packed full of millions of copies of elements called transposons and other repeated sequences.

It might be expected that evolution would kick this stuff out, through the process of natural selection. If a stretch of DNA is useful, it sticks around and becomes a permanent part of the genome. But if not... well, it actually sticks around anyway, because evolution is a slow and imperfect process. More recent research actually suggests that this 'junk' DNA may not be completely useless.

Some researchers actually think that our abundance of non-coding DNA is the biological equivalent of bubble wrap, acting as protective packing around our genes and helping to dilute the impact of cancer-causing agents such as X-rays and other carcinogens. It may even be that some of the junk is structural, helping to space genes and their control switches out in the right way, although this theory is extremely hard to prove. Using genetic engineering techniques, researchers can 'glue' a gene right next to the switch that activates it and it still works, suggesting that the precise spacing isn't all that important.

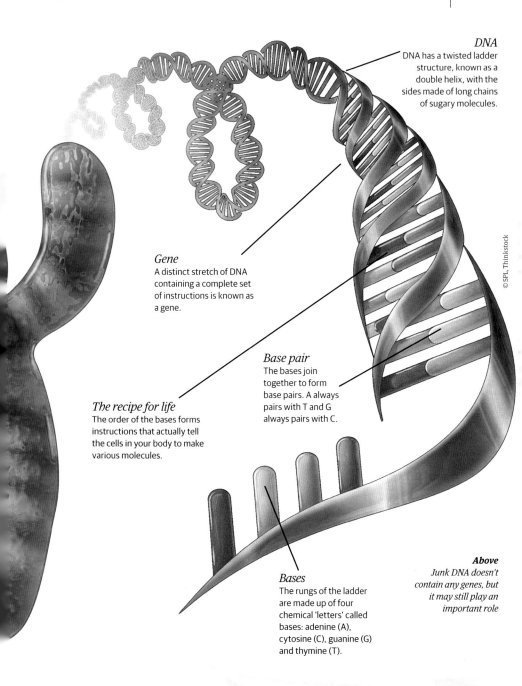

DNA
DNA has a twisted ladder structure, known as a double helix, with the sides made of long chains of sugary molecules.

© SPL, Thinkstock

Gene
A distinct stretch of DNA containing a complete set of instructions is known as a gene.

The recipe for life
The order of the bases forms instructions that actually tell the cells in your body to make various molecules.

Base pair
The bases join together to form base pairs. A always pairs with T and G always pairs with C.

Bases
The rungs of the ladder are made up of four chemical 'letters' called bases: adenine (A), cytosine (C), guanine (G) and thymine (T).

Above
Junk DNA doesn't contain any genes, but it may still play an important role

What is the science behind radioactive dating?

Learn how scientists measure time using Earth's rocks

Most chemical elements remain stable over time, but there are radioactive variants of common atoms, and these are unstable. As the years pass, they gradually decay. One of the most well-known is carbon-14, which has two extra neutrons in its nucleus. Atoms of carbon-14 cannot hold on to the extra neutrons forever, and over time they will lose them to form stable, non-radioactive nitrogen-14. This decay happens at a fixed rate, like the ticking of a clock, and is known as a half-life: the time it takes for half the unstable atoms in a given mass to decay.

The carbon-14 clock allows scientists to determine the age of fossilised remains of living things. All life on Earth is carbon-based, and when animals and plants are living, they incorporate traces of naturally occurring radioactive carbon into their tissues. When they die, this process stops, and the carbon clock starts ticking. When we dig up fossils years, or even millennia later, some of this carbon will have decayed, so by measuring the amount that is left, we can tell how old the samples are.

Each of these rock clocks all tick at completely different rates. When magma solidifies to form igneous rocks, it traps radioactive potassium-40, which takes 1.25 billion years to tick down by half. Uranium-238 takes 4.5 billion years, thorium-232 takes 14 billion years and rubidium-87 takes 48.8 billion years.

⮞ *Carbon dating* ⮜
This form of radioactive dating is used to pinpoint the age of once living things

2 Fossil
When living organisms die, they stop making new molecules, ensuring that no new carbon-14 is added to their remains.

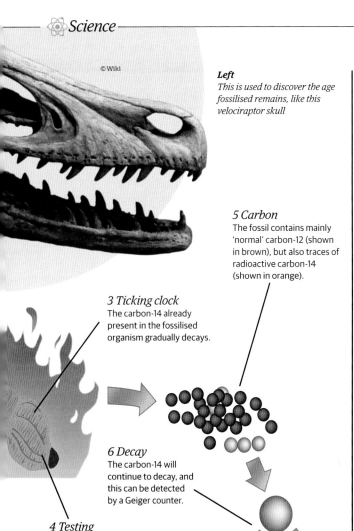

© Wiki

Left
This is used to discover the age fossilised remains, like this velociraptor skull

5 Carbon
The fossil contains mainly 'normal' carbon-12 (shown in brown), but also traces of radioactive carbon-14 (shown in orange).

3 Ticking clock
The carbon-14 already present in the fossilised organism gradually decays.

6 Decay
The carbon-14 will continue to decay, and this can be detected by a Geiger counter.

4 Testing
To find the age of a fossil, scientists remove a small piece and burn it to release the carbon as carbon dioxide gas.

Nitrogen   *Electron*

1 Living organism
Over the course of their lifetimes, living organisms incorporate small amounts of naturally occurring radioactive carbon-14 into their tissues.

7 Proportions
The older the fossil is, the less carbon-14 will still be present in the sample.

≈ What is a half-life? ≈

The reason that radioactive atoms can be used as clocks is because they decay at a predictable rate. However, waiting for radioactive decay is a bit like waiting for corn kernels to pop. We know approximately how long it should take for all the corn to become popcorn, but we can't predict which kernel will pop first.

In the same way, we don't know exactly when radioactive clocks will tick, but we do know the time it takes for half of the atoms in a sample to decay. This is known as the 'half life', and for carbon-14, it is 5,730 years.

The half-life is not affected by things like temperature, pressure, or other environmental influences, meaning that, whatever was going on in the world at the time, these molecular clocks would continue ticking, keeping time and allowing scientists to look back and figure out how old things are.

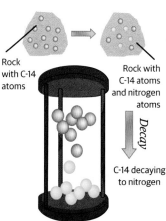

Rock with C-14 atoms

Rock with C-14 atoms and nitrogen atoms

Decay

C-14 decaying to nitrogen

Above
By measuring the chemical make-up of a rock, we can tell how long the clock has been ticking

How does baking bread work?

How chemistry and biology help to make the perfect loaf

Ancient Egyptian hieroglyphs show that humans have been baking bread for thousands of years. The first attempts consisted of ground wheat and water that was left to harden in the Sun. It's possible that one mixture was left longer than usual and the naturally occurring yeasts enabled the dough to ferment. The resulting loaf would have risen, leading the Egyptians on a mission to isolate the yeast so that it could be added to every batch of bread. This key ingredient is just a part of the amazing chemical and biological processes that create a food enjoyed all over the world.

~ *Making bread with science* ~

A step-by-step guide to harnessing the power of yeast for a light, fluffy texture

Mix the ingredients
Put flour, yeast, salt and water into a bowl and mix together to form dough. Flour when combined with water, forms gluten. This gives dough its stretchy, and almost elastic properties.

Start kneading
Place the dough on a flour-covered surface and press it with the palm of your hand before folding it over, turning it and repeating again and again. You can stop kneading when the dough has a smooth, elastic surface.

Let it rise
Place the dough in a clean bowl, cover with cling film and leave it in a warm place. The yeast feeds on sugars in the flour, producing carbon dioxide which gets trapped and forms bubbles, so the dough rises.

Knock back the dough
Once the dough has doubled in size, take it out of the bowl and gently knead it again. This will knock out some of the air to get rid of any large bubbles. Now leave the dough to double in size again.

Bake in the oven
Heat causes the gases to expand and increase in size. The yeast dies and the gluten and starch solidify so the dough can't expand further. Leaving a light and fluffy centre, and the sugars caramelise to form a crust.

≈ *What is yeast?* ≈

Discover how yeast makes bread possible

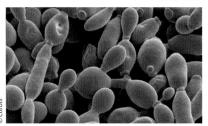

© Corbis

Above
Baking yeast is typically a species called Saccharomyces cerevisiae, which is also used to make beer

It's strange to think that you are adding a living organism into your bread dough, especially when you consider it is actually a fungus. Thankfully though, the packets of yeast you buy at the supermarket contain a different species from the ones that cause nasty infections. Baker's yeast usually comes in the form of capsules made from dried yeast. When these capsules come into contact with moisture, the shells dissolve to release the live yeast inside. This gets to work feeding on the sugar created by enzymes that digest the starch content of the flour. As well as carbon dioxide, this process also produces alcohol, which burns off during baking but leaves behind a slightly sour flavour. Yeast works best at warm temperatures, so it is best to leave the dough to rise in a warm place, but cover it to prevent the moisture from evaporating.

≈ *The tanning process* ≈

Learn about the important structures within the skin that play a role in creating a tan

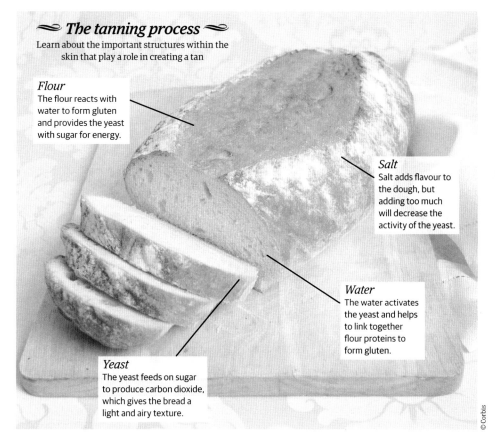

Flour
The flour reacts with water to form gluten and provides the yeast with sugar for energy.

Salt
Salt adds flavour to the dough, but adding too much will decrease the activity of the yeast.

Water
The water activates the yeast and helps to link together flour proteins to form gluten.

Yeast
The yeast feeds on sugar to produce carbon dioxide, which gives the bread a light and airy texture.

© Corbis

Why do baked beans give you wind?

You can blame it on the bacteria in your gut

Below
Baked beans actually contain sugars that our bodies struggle to digest

Baked beans are a tasty treat that are high in fibre and therefore extremely good for your digestive system. However, as they make their way through your body, they also produce an unfortunate side effect: flatulence. This bodily function is a result of sugars called oligosaccharides that are contained within the beans. These sugar molecules are too big to be absorbed in our small intestines, and our bodies do not produce the enzyme that can break them down, so they carry on through to the large intestines intact and undigested. Here, they're met by our gut bacteria, which have no problem breaking them down into something more manageable. As they do this, they produce gasses including hydrogen and methane, which gradually accumulate in your lower intestine and escape through your rectum as flatulence.

© Dreamstime

What happens when you eat too much?

Learn about the effects of an all-you-can eat buffet

When you've just polished off a plate piled high with food, it can sometimes feel like you're going to explode. Although it is possible for your stomach to rupture after overeating, your gag reflex is likely to kick in long before you actually reach that point. The average human stomach can handle between one and one-and-a-half litres of food before getting the urge to throw it back up, but can stretch to accommodate four times that much before a rupture occurs.

Right
Overeating can damage your brain's ability to tell you when you're full

© Thinkstock

≈ *Ready to pop* ≈

How does your stomach cope with a big meal?

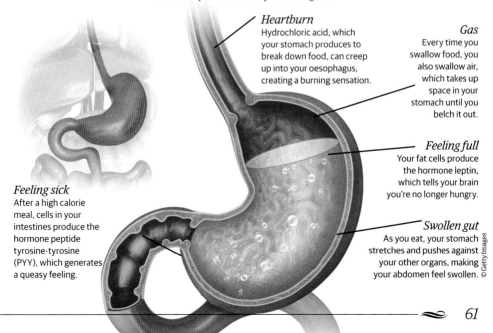

Heartburn
Hydrochloric acid, which your stomach produces to break down food, can creep up into your oesophagus, creating a burning sensation.

Gas
Every time you swallow food, you also swallow air, which takes up space in your stomach until you belch it out.

Feeling full
Your fat cells produce the hormone leptin, which tells your brain you're no longer hungry.

Feeling sick
After a high calorie meal, cells in your intestines produce the hormone peptide tyrosine-tyrosine (PYY), which generates a queasy feeling.

Swollen gut
As you eat, your stomach stretches and pushes against your other organs, making your abdomen feel swollen.

© Getty Images

What is the biology of hunger?

Grab a snack, and then find out what's really going on in your rumbling tummy

Below
The stress hormone, cortisol, can increase appetite and cause a person to overeat

The feeling is too familiar: a growling in the pit of your stomach that starts around late morning when breakfast is just a memory and lunchtime is still a tiny speck on the horizon. It's hunger - a feeling that begins with the hormone known as ghrelin. Once your body has finished digesting and using up the energy from your last meal, your blood sugar and insulin levels drop. In response, ghrelin is produced in the gut and travels to the brain, letting it know that sustenance is needed. The brain then commands the release of a second hormone called neuropeptide Y, which stimulates appetite.

Once you have eaten, nerves in your stomach sense stretching, letting your brain know you're full. Cholecystokinin improves digestion by slowing down food being emptied from the stomach into the small intestine, as well as stimulating the production of molecules that help to break down food. GLP-1 tells the pancreas to release more insulin and also reduces appetite. PYY is secreted into the bloodstream by the small intestine after eating, binding to receptors in the brain to make you feel full.

Once all of the food is digested, the hunger cycle continues

© Dreamstime.Thinkstock

∼ *Hungry hormones* ∼

Whether you're a bit peckish or totally ravenous, it's all down to the hormones in your system

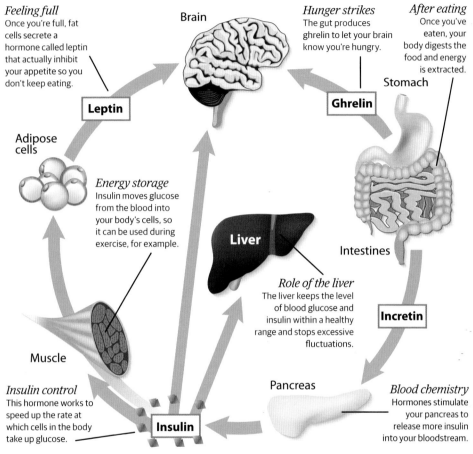

Feeling full
Once you're full, fat cells secrete a hormone called leptin that actually inhibit your appetite so you don't keep eating.

Brain

Hunger strikes
The gut produces ghrelin to let your brain know you're hungry.

After eating
Once you've eaten, your body digests the food and energy is extracted.

Stomach

Leptin

Ghrelin

Adipose cells

Energy storage
Insulin moves glucose from the blood into your body's cells, so it can be used during exercise, for example.

Liver

Intestines

Role of the liver
The liver keeps the level of blood glucose and insulin within a healthy range and stops excessive fluctuations.

Incretin

Muscle

Insulin control
This hormone works to speed up the rate at which cells in the body take up glucose.

Insulin

Pancreas

Blood chemistry
Hormones stimulate your pancreas to release more insulin into your bloodstream.

∼ *When the mind takes over...* ∼

When our minds get involved in craving food, it's a whole different story.

There's not much nutritional value in a bacon sandwich or a donut, for example, so it's not a 'need' for a treat, it's a 'want'. This is because the very first time you experienced a donut, the mesolimbic centre of your brain (the region that processes pleasure) lit up, as the treat released chemicals known as opioids that bind with receptors in the brain. Triggering the release of dopamine, the feel-good hormone. It's actually the same one that is released when we fall in love!

What are muscle cramps?

What causes these unexpected and painful spasms?

Cramp occurs when your muscles involuntarily contract very quickly and do not relax again straight away. These sudden spasms commonly affect the calves and last just a few seconds, but can persist for 15 agonising minutes or more. Normally, your calf muscles contract to raise your heels and relax to lower them, allowing you to walk, run and jump. However, during a cramp these muscles contract tightly and unexpectedly, leaving you unable to control them until the contraction subsides. The affected muscles will continue

⇌ **What causes cramp?** ⇋

The leading theory suggests that disrupted nerve signals may be to blame

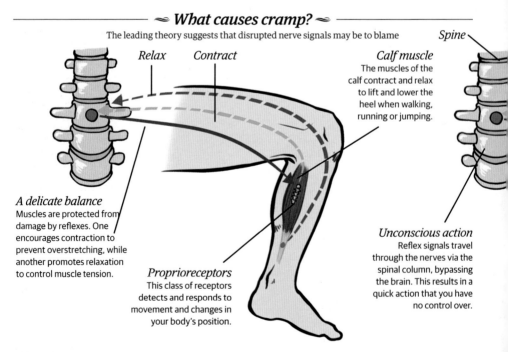

Relax   *Contract*

Spine

Calf muscle
The muscles of the calf contract and relax to lift and lower the heel when walking, running or jumping.

A delicate balance
Muscles are protected from damage by reflexes. One encourages contraction to prevent overstretching, while another promotes relaxation to control muscle tension.

Proprioreceptors
This class of receptors detects and responds to movement and changes in your body's position.

Unconscious action
Reflex signals travel through the nerves via the spinal column, bypassing the brain. This results in a quick action that you have no control over.

to remain tense, tender and painful while they are refusing to relax.

Despite being such a common experience, nobody knows exactly what causes these random contractions. It's thought that excessive strain on the muscles or a restriction in blood supply could be contributing factors, but one of the most prevalent theories is that cramps are actually caused by abnormal nerve activity.

Receptors within muscles and tendons constantly monitor the body's movement and position. These receptors send reflex signals to protect the muscles from potential damage. One reflex encourages muscle contraction, to prevent overstretching, while the other promotes relaxation to control tension. These reflexes are normally balanced, but can be disrupted so that the contraction signal overwhelms the relaxation one, resulting in the unexpected, intense and painful muscle spasm of cramp.

They are often associated with exercise, but according to the NHS, 75 per cent of leg cramp cases occur during sleep.

©Thinkstock

Above
*Even elite athletes can
be floored mid-stride
by cramp*

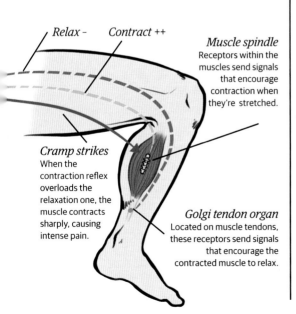

Relax –   *Contract ++*

Muscle spindle
Receptors within the muscles send signals that encourage contraction when they're stretched.

Cramp strikes
When the contraction reflex overloads the relaxation one, the muscle contracts sharply, causing intense pain.

Golgi tendon organ
Located on muscle tendons, these receptors send signals that encourage the contracted muscle to relax.

≈ *Types of cramp* ≈

Apart from being an inconvenience, cramps are generally harmless. However, if they persist for more than 15 minutes, or reoccur regularly, they may be a symptom of an underlying problem.

Leg cramps are divided into two categories: idiopathic or secondary. Idiopathic leg cramps seemingly happen for no reason, like those that occur just as you're drifting off to sleep. Secondary leg cramps are related to pre-existing conditions or particular activities, such as infections, neurological disorders, strenuous exercise or dehydration. Pregnant women may also become vulnerable to cramps, as the weight of the growing foetus puts strain on their legs.

What is the science behind stress?

Discover what happens when you to get stressed

Below
The hypothalamus is the control centre of the stress response in the brain

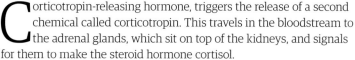

Corticotropin-releasing hormone, triggers the release of a second chemical called corticotropin. This travels in the bloodstream to the adrenal glands, which sit on top of the kidneys, and signals for them to make the steroid hormone cortisol.

Cortisol is also known as the 'stress hormone', and it has effects all across the body. It helps to return systems to normal during times of stress, including raising blood sugar, balancing pH and suppressing the immune system. Vasopressin also travels in the blood to the kidneys, but its function is slightly different. It increases the re-uptake of water, decreasing the amount of urine produced and helping the body to hold on to the reserves that it has.

Why do my knuckles crack more when it's cold?

Learn the science behind why your knuckles pop

Below
MRI scans revealed the real cause of cracking knuckles

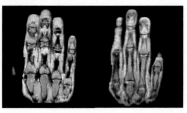

In 2015, researchers at the University of Alberta, Canada showed once and for all that the cracking sound made in finger joints is down to the formation of bubbles. As you pull, the surfaces of the joint come apart and a cavity appears in the fluid between. This makes the noise. To crack your knuckles again, you have to wait for the bubble to disappear. The researchers didn't look at the effect of climate, but it could be that something about the cold effects the behaviour of the fluid in your joints, helping the bubbles to disperse more rapidly.

How do cavities form?

*Avoid a trip to the dentist by learning
about how to prevent tooth decay*

Harmful bacteria inside your mouth feed on the sugars contained within the food you eat, and in the process produce acid that erodes the hard tooth enamel. If left alone, it will group together to form a sticky substance called plaque. As the plaque absorbs minerals in your saliva, it hardens to form tartar, which protects the bacteria so they can continue to erode your teeth and form deep holes known as cavities. As they expose the sensitive inner layers of your tooth, cavities can be very painful.

Right
Bacteria erodes your teeth and forms deep holes which are known as cavities

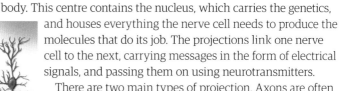

What are nerve cells?

Find out what the electrical wiring within your body is

Nerve cells, or neurones all have some key features in common, but they also have their own specialisms.
Many nerve cells can be divided into four categories: pseudo-unipolar, bipolar, multipolar, and pyramidal. These categories are based on the number of extensions that stick out from the cell body. This centre contains the nucleus, which carries the genetics, and houses everything the nerve cell needs to produce the molecules that do its job. The projections link one nerve cell to the next, carrying messages in the form of electrical signals, and passing them on using neurotransmitters.

There are two main types of projection. Axons are often long and tube-shaped, and carry messages away from the cell body, while dendrites are short and tapered, and receive signals from other nerve cells.

Below
Nerve cells are divided into four different categories

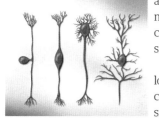

© SPL, Thinkstock, Corbis, Dreamstime

What are meteorological satellites?

The spacecraft keeping a watchful eye on Earth to help us predict the weather

Weather forecasting isn't just handy for letting you know if you need an umbrella, it can also help save lives by providing early warning of devastating storms and floods. To be able to accurately predict these events, forecasters need to constantly monitor the Earth's surface and atmosphere, and they can do this thanks to a vast network of meteorological satellites flying through space. There are two main types: geostationary and polar-orbiting satellites, which work together to monitor the planet from every angle. Currently watching North and South America and the Eastern Pacific are the Geostationary Operational Environmental Satellites, GOES-EAST and GOES-WEST. The current GOES-EAST satellite, GOES-13, is actually set to retire after ten years of service. Its new replacement, GOES-R, will be able to provide 50 times more information, helping forecasters predict the weather more accurately than they ever have before.

Right
GOES-R is to be renamed GOES-16 after launch

∼ *Next-generation weather satellite?* ∼
How GOES-R will monitor the weather in amazing detail

Solar array
Five separate solar panels will deploy into a single, rotating wing to provide electricity for the satellite's instruments.

Geostationary Lightning Mapper (GLM)
By monitoring the presence of lightning, GLM will provide early predictions of storms and other severe weather events.

Advanced Baseline Imager (ABI)
ABI will measure the visible and infrared light reflected by the Earth to monitor clouds, atmosphere and surface.

Solar Ultraviolet Imager (SUVI)
SUVI will create regular images of the Sun to help us forecast space weather that could disturb Earth's magnetic field.

Extreme Ultraviolet and X-Ray Irradiance Sensors (EXIS)
This instrument monitors the Sun's electromagnetic radiation to detect solar flares that can even interrupt communication and navigation systems.

Space Environment In-Situ Suite (SEISS)
Four sensors monitoring proton, electron and heavy ion fluxes in space will highlight any radiation hazards to astronauts and spacecraft.

Star tracker
By pinpointing its location using the position of the stars, the satellite's thrusters can manoeuvre in orbit.

Unique Payload Services (UPS)
Transponders communicate with other satellites for more geographically complete monitoring.

Antennas
The data collected by GOES-R will be sent back to Earth for processing via a series of antennas.

Magnetometer
Able to detect charged particles that can be dangerous to spacecraft.

Combined
Combing visible and infrared data helps show Earth's features and their temperatures in greater detail.

Visible
The clouds reflect more light and so appear brighter than the land and sea.

Infrared
Features with hotter temperatures appear darker whereas cold areas are bright.

© NASA, GOES-R

What are constellations?

Without making patterns, our night sky would be a confusion of stars

While we know that the stars are many light years away, and all at different distances, astronomers still put them into groupings called constellations. These are named after the characters, animals and objects they resemble.

The constellations help us make sense of the night sky. Without them, it would be a chaotic sprinkling of stars, constellations give astronomers a quick and visual way of getting their bearings in the cosmos.

Below
There are 88 official constellations

There are 88 official constellations and these provide the catalogue names of the stars. For example, Deneb is the brightest star in the constellation Cygnus, so this is known as Alpha Cygni. The brightest star in Boötes is Arcturus, so it is also called Alpha Boötis. The Andromeda galaxy is in the constellation of Andromeda, so seasoned stargazers will know the rough area of the sky in which to look.

You'll probably have heard of the Zodiac constellations - Capricorn, Aquarius, Pisces and so on, plotted along the path that the Sun moves through each year. Your sign is the constellation that the Sun was in at the time of your birth.

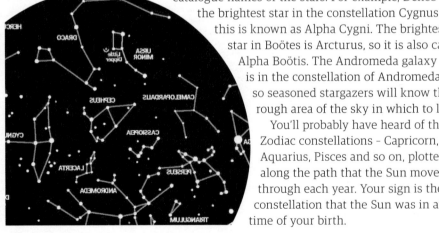

∾ *Distances to the stars of Orion* ∾

Orion might look like a flat blanket of stars, but its components are spread over hundreds of light years

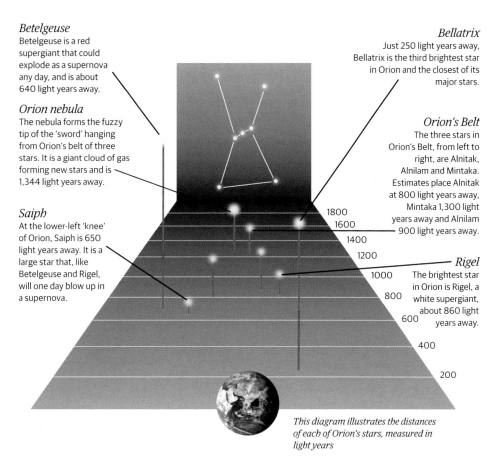

Betelgeuse
Betelgeuse is a red supergiant that could explode as a supernova any day, and is about 640 light years away.

Orion nebula
The nebula forms the fuzzy tip of the 'sword' hanging from Orion's belt of three stars. It is a giant cloud of gas forming new stars and is 1,344 light years away.

Saiph
At the lower-left 'knee' of Orion, Saiph is 650 light years away. It is a large star that, like Betelgeuse and Rigel, will one day blow up in a supernova.

Bellatrix
Just 250 light years away, Bellatrix is the third brightest star in Orion and the closest of its major stars.

Orion's Belt
The three stars in Orion's Belt, from left to right, are Alnitak, Alnilam and Mintaka. Estimates place Alnitak at 800 light years away, Mintaka 1,300 light years away and Alnilam 900 light years away.

Rigel
The brightest star in Orion is Rigel, a white supergiant, about 860 light years away.

1800
1600
1400
1200
1000
800
600
400
200

This diagram illustrates the distances of each of Orion's stars, measured in light years

∾ *Origins of constellations* ∾

Civilisations going back to ancient times are thought to have charted the constellations. At first, these patterns of stars were used for astrological predictions and navigation, as well as for communication among astronomers. However, as the modern field of astronomy developed, it was soon discovered that different culturally nominated constellations made communication tricky. To solve the problem, the IAU divided the sky into 88 different constellations between the Northern and Southern Hemisphere and gave them names that are now universally accepted.

What is 'Young Jupiter'?

How a new exoplanet could reveal secrets of the Solar System

Below
This artist's impression of 51 Eridani b shows hot layers glowing through a cloudy atmosphere

In a distant solar system 100 light years away, scientists have discovered an exoplanet that seems oddly familiar. 51 Eridani b is a gas giant roughly 11 times wider than Earth, and is similar to our Solar System's very own Jupiter. However, the new discovery, made using the Gemini Planet Imager, is only 20 million years old – a blink of an eye compared to 4.5-billion-year-old Jupiter! With more tests, scientists could uncover how it came into existence and then that knowledge could be used to understand how Jupiter was formed. Even at 427 degrees Celsius (800 degrees Fahrenheit), this so-called 'young Jupiter' is actually relatively cold and small compared to other gas giant exoplanet discoveries. This suggests that rather than material collapsing quickly to form a hot planet, 51 Eridani b's core built up gradually. This slower growth process would mean its formation has more in common with Jupiter's. Further investigation is needed to see whether 51 Eridani b can help us understand how the planets in our own Solar System came into being.

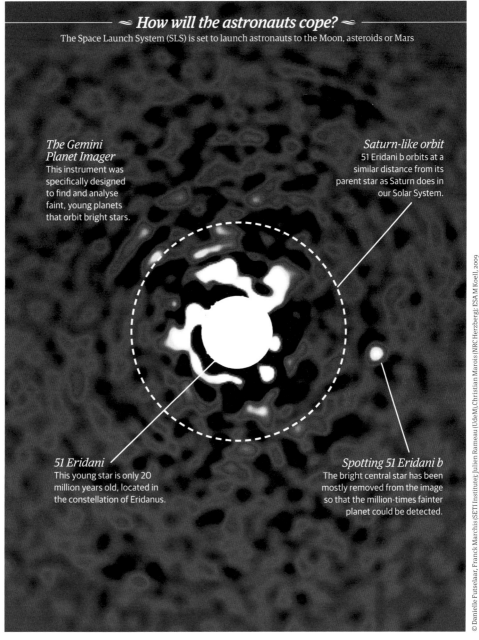

≈ *How will the astronauts cope?* ≈

The Space Launch System (SLS) is set to launch astronauts to the Moon, asteroids or Mars

*The Gemini
Planet Imager*
This instrument was
specifically designed
to find and analyse
faint, young planets
that orbit bright stars.

Saturn-like orbit
51 Eridani b orbits at a
similar distance from its
parent star as Saturn does in
our Solar System.

51 Eridani
This young star is only 20
million years old, located in
the constellation of Eridanus.

Spotting 51 Eridani b
The bright central star has been
mostly removed from the image
so that the million-times fainter
planet could be detected.

Do other planets have seasons?

Are there seasons on any other planets?

Other planets experience seasons, although these typically look nothing like our planet's. Our seasons are caused by the 23-degree tilt in Earth's axis of rotation, exposing its hemispheres to different amounts of sunlight. Planets with a very slight tilt, such as Jupiter, have very small variations across the year. At the other extreme, with an 82-degree tilt, Uranus's hemispheres lean away from the Sun for decades at a time before swapping over. When spring comes after each 20-year winter, huge storms are triggered in its atmosphere. Other planets also experience differences due to the size and shape of their orbits (orbital eccentricity). A shorter orbit, such as Venus's, results in a much shorter year and shorter seasons. Unlike Earth, which has an almost circular orbit, Mars is ten per cent closer to the Sun during its northern hemisphere's winter than summer, giving rise to differences in the seasons undergone by either hemisphere.

Below
Seasons on other planets look nothing like our own

Can you blow bubbles in space?

Discover if its possible to blow galactic bubbles

In the vacuum of space, blowing a bubble is impossible. For a start, there is no air to blow into bubbles, but even if you brought your own, it wouldn't work. To create a bubble, the air pressure inside and outside need to be equal. In space, there is no pressure, so the bubble would burst instantly. However, you could blow bubbles on a spacecraft, and they would actually last longer. On Earth, gravity pulls the soap downwards, causing the top of the bubble to thin out and burst. In zero gravity, the thickness would remain equal, so the bubble wouldn't pop so easily.

Right
Water naturally forms into floating bubbles that never pop in zero gravity

How do astronauts float?

Why are astronauts weightless inside the ISS?

Below
ISS astronauts and the objects around them are in a constant state of free-fall

ISS astronauts are not truly weightless as they are still in fact affected by the Earth's gravitational pull, but due to the lack of other forces pushing on them leads to the perceived sensation of complete weightlessness.

Down here on planet Earth we experience gravity on a daily basis, as well as opposing contact forces. These forces are exerted through the ground we stand on, and give us a sense of our own weight.

The ISS is in orbit around the Earth, meaning that it is actually constantly 'falling' towards the Earth. It is in this state of perpetual free-fall that astronauts don't experience any contact forces, and therefore they end up feeling weightless.

© NASA

What is weather like in space?

Get the forecast for the Sun's explosive activity and how it affects us on Earth

The Sun, and the vast vacuum of space surrounding it, may seem pretty peaceful to us on Earth, but it is actually alive with violent activity. Although you might not hear about it on television forecasts, it's the source of a variety of space weather, and there are some very important reasons why we should be aware of it. Throughout its 11-year solar cycle, the big ball of hot plasma at the centre of our Solar System bombards our planet with solar winds. During periods of peak activity, this can disrupt many of the technological systems we rely on for communication, navigation and more. Read on to discover how...

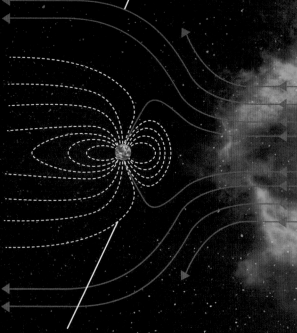

Solar wind

Streams of charged particles called plasma are constantly escaping the surface of the Sun, as the star's powerful gravity fails to contain them. Known as solar wind, it can reach speeds of up to 800 kilometres per second as it hurtles towards Earth, where it continuously batters our planet's magnetic field. Solar wind is so powerful that it is believed to have stripped away the atmospheres of many other planets, such as Mercury, but Earth's relatively strong magnetic field is keeping it at bay.

Earth's protection

Earth's magnetic field forms a magnetosphere, which acts as a shield to protect our planet from the effects of space weather. However, the constant battering of solar winds has had a dramatic impact on its shape, compressing the side closest to the Sun and stretching out the other. Sometimes, the solar winds can disconnect the magnetic field lines on the night side, and when they snap back into position, they push charged particles back towards Earth's upper atmosphere.

Solar flares

When twisting magnetic field lines in sunspot regions cross and reconnect with one another, they cause massive explosions called solar flares. The energy released is the equivalent of millions of 100-megaton hydrogen bombs exploding at the same time, sending huge amounts of radiation out into the Solar System. The radiation emitted spans across the entire electromagnetic spectrum, from radio waves to X-rays and gamma rays, and travels at the speed of light to reach Earth in just eight minutes.

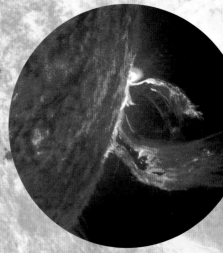

Coronal mass ejections

The magnetic field lines that produce solar flares sometimes become so twisted that they actually snap and reconnect at other points. The gaps that form can no longer hold plasma on the Sun's surface, and release billions of tons of it into space as a 'coronal mass ejection'. Their speed can vary greatly, meaning they can reach Earth in a matter of hours or days, and when they do their own magnetic field slams into Earth's to generate geomagnetic storms.

Sunspots

Magnetic field lines breaking through the Sun's surface create dark regions known as sunspots. As heat is inhibited from rising up from the solar interior, these regions are comparatively cooler than the rest of the Sun's surface, but still reach scorching temperatures of around 3,500 degrees Celsius. Sunspots are usually found near to the Sun's equator and are the source of most extreme space weather. The number of them varies throughout the 11-year solar cycle, creating periods of peak activity.

© NASA

Do astronauts feel alone in space?

Astronauts have to be physically fit, but mental preparation is just as important

Space is vast, empty and lonely. Onboard a ship with just a handful of other human beings for company, journeys to other worlds in our Solar System will test more than just the physical bodies of the astronauts. They will need to be able to cope with extreme isolation.

No human being has ever travelled more than 400,171 kilometres from the surface of the Earth, little more than a couple of days away. People have spent months and months on the International Space Station, but home is just below and always in sight - travelling to other planets will be very different.

Mars is 225 million kilometres away and will take a crew seven months to get there, and they will only have one another for support, there will be no emergency evacuation, and they will not be able to step outside and feel the air on their skin. They will have to work in a harsh environment, completing monotonous tasks day after day, and although they will be on one of the most exciting missions in the history of humankind, it is going to be a tough and gruelling journey.

Astronauts are already thoroughly screened to ensure that they are able to withstand the stresses and challenges of space travel, but extra precautions are being taken before a crew makes this bold leap into the unknown. On Earth, trainee crews are simulating the isolation of long-term space travel in specially designed habitats to make sure they are up to the challenge that lies ahead.

Above
Astronaut Tim Peake's photograph of the Alps from onboard the ISS, where planet Earth is always in sight, but out of reach

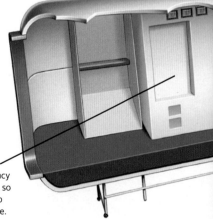

Medical station
There is no emergency evacuation in space, so the crew will need to be able to cope alone.

≈ *Deep space training* ≈

The only way to prepare for isolation is to experience it

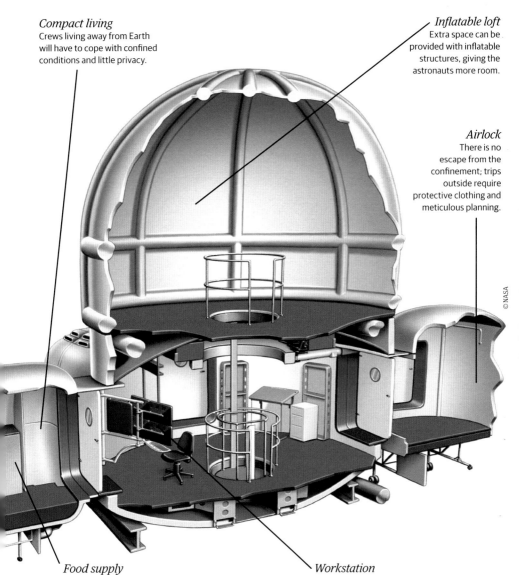

Compact living
Crews living away from Earth
will have to cope with confined
conditions and little privacy.

Inflatable loft
Extra space can be
provided with inflatable
structures, giving the
astronauts more room.

Airlock
There is no
escape from the
confinement; trips
outside require
protective clothing and
meticulous planning.

© NASA

Food supply
The range of foods available will be limited, and astronauts
may end up eating the same things again and again.

Workstation
Days off are not always an option; crews will
need to be prepared to perform essential tasks.

How do astronaut train for space?

The best place on Earth to prepare for zero gravity is a swimming pool

When an astronaut prepares for a mission to the International Space Station, they must practise the tasks that they'll be carrying out in space. However, in order to make the training as realistic as possible, the microgravity they'll encounter outside our planet's atmosphere needs to be mimicked here on Earth.

NASA has an ingenious way of replicating space's unique environment on our home planet - it has placed a large-scale mock-up of the ISS in an enormous swimming pool. The American space agency calls this 12-metre (40-foot) deep pool the Neutral Buoyancy Lab (NBL) and astronauts have been training here since 1996.

Astronauts undertake six-to-eight-hour underwater sessions on a daily basis. When it's time to begin training, a camera diver shadows the astronaut to capture everything that happens, so it can be reviewed later. Safety divers are also on-hand at all times and the astronaut is rigged up to various support systems for air, power and communications.

Underwater, the trainee astronaut is breathing nitrox air, which is comprised of 46 per cent oxygen. This increased oxygen concentration reduces the risk of decompression sickness. Long tethers also enable an astronaut to lock themselves onto handrails while they are practising a task. Everything they do underwater is a simulation of what they'll be doing onboard the ISS.

Below
In the Neutral Buoyancy Laboratory, astronauts train for up to eight hours a day underwater

≈ *Size does matter* ≈

An essential piece of clothing for space travel, each part of a spacesuit
has an important job

Before getting in the water for a session in the Neutral Buoyancy Laboratory, an astronaut has to dress for the part. During the fitting for their space suit, there are 36 measurements taken of their bodies and 46 measurements of their hands, while plenty of padding inside the suit ensures they don't slip around. The end result is so heavy – weighing almost as much as two men - that several technicians are required to help the astronaut get suited and booted.

≈ *Pool-sized space environment* ≈

In the Neutral Buoyancy Laboratory, astronauts can get a taster of
what working in space will feel like

Voluminous
The pool contains an enormous amount of water: 28 million litres (6.2 million gallons) – the same as ten Olympic swimming pools!

Neutral buoyancy
The water provides 'neutral buoyancy', so astronauts who are training neither rise nor sink, simulating the effect of zero gravity.

Hidden depths
The NBL is 61.6m (202ft) long by 31m (102ft) wide, but it still can't fit the entire ISS inside.

Life support
Astronauts are connected to the pool's life support systems that provide air, power and communications, by 26m (85ft) long tethers.

Sunken space station
A mock-up of the International Space Station's modules lies 12m (40ft) deep in the water.

Safety
In 115,000 hours of dives, there has never been an accident with an astronaut. They are supported by a team of safety divers and cameramen.

Breathing underwater
In order to avoid decompression sickness, astronauts in the pool need to breathe nitrox air that is 46 per cent pure oxygen.

© NASA

What is a pulsar?

The truth behind the 'alien beacons'

When pulsars were discovered in 1967 by Jocelyn Bell, nobody knew what they were. They were so mysterious that the first pulsar was half-jokingly nicknamed 'LGM-1', for Little Green Men. Today, however, we know that pulsars have nothing to do with aliens, but come from something just as dramatic. They are the rapidly spinning condensed cores of massive stars that have exploded as supernovae.

When a star greater than eight times the mass of our Sun reaches the end of its life, it stops generating energy from fusion power within its core. This causes the core to collapse into an object so dense that electrons and protons merge to form neutrons. The outer layers of the star quickly fall onto this collapsed core before a shock wave blows them back out, causing the star to explode. The core survives, however, as a 'star' of neutrons about 20 kilometres across.

This neutron star is highly magnetic and is born spinning. Its magnetic field funnels away charged particles along two jets bursting out from its magnetic poles. As the neutron star spins, these jets spin with it, flashing in our direction. We see them as a rapid sequence of light pulses - a pulsar.

Field strength
A pulsar's magnetic field is impressive - it is 10 trillion times stronger than Earth's.

Ultra-dense
A pulsar is so dense that a teaspoonful of it would have the same mass as a mountain.

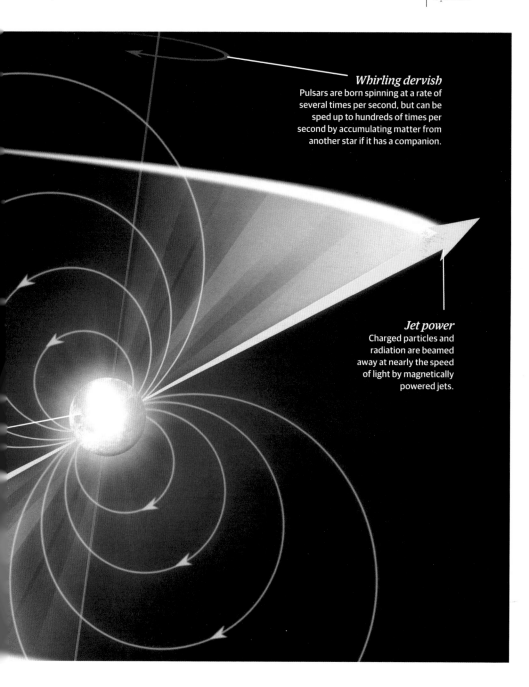

Whirling dervish
Pulsars are born spinning at a rate of
several times per second, but can be
sped up to hundreds of times per
second by accumulating matter from
another star if it has a companion.

Jet power
Charged particles and
radiation are beamed
away at nearly the speed
of light by magnetically
powered jets.

How far can we send a spacecraft before we lose contact?

What's behind that mysterious glint in the sky?

How far a space probe can go before communication is lost is limited only by the radio technology we develop. Voyager 1, launched in 1977, is currently over 20 billion kilometres away, but we are still able to exchange information with it using radio signals. On Earth, huge antennae pointed towards the spacecraft amplifies its weak signals. Advances in this technology have allowed us to receive transmissions far longer than expected, and newer spacecrafts with more powerful transmitters could extend this range even further. We will lose contact with Voyager when it runs out of energy in around 2025.

© NASA

What is the interstellar medium?

*The space between the stars may not be as empty
as we once thought*

Even the emptiest voids between the stars contain gas and dust, known as the interstellar medium (ISM). Ninety-nine per cent of the ISM is made up of hydrogen and helium gas, but at an extremely low density. The remaining one per cent is interstellar dust, which consists of extremely small particles of carbon or silicate. These tiny grains are formed in relatively cool and dense environments, such as in the outer atmospheres of red giants. When they are ejected by solar winds, radiation pressure, or in stellar explosions, these grains become scattered across the galaxy.

Right
In this Hubble image, the interstellar gas glows blue as it is blasted by strong stellar winds

© ESO/M: NASA, Goddard Space Flight Center; NASA/Van Allen probes/Goddard Space
Flight Center; NASA/ESA/The Hubble Heritage Team

Why is the Moon slowly moving away from us?

Discover how our Moon is moving away from Earth

Right
The Moon's drift is related to ocean tides

The action of ocean tides is causing the Moon to gradually drift away from Earth. The Moon's gravitational pull on our planet's water creates a bulge on the ocean surface on the side of the Earth that is closest. This bulge in turn exerts a gravitational pull on the Moon. As the Earth rotates, the bulge moves forward in relation to the Moon. As a result, the Earth's rotation slows slightly, giving a little bit of energy to the Moon, pushing it away. Each year, the Moon edges about 3.78 centimetres further away.

How can we see back in time?

When we look into space, we are actually looking into the past

Below
When this light was emitted by Andromeda, our ancestors hadn't even learnt to use fire

© NASA

If the Sun suddenly vanished, it would take a full eight minutes and 20 seconds for anyone to notice. This is because sunlight does not reach us instantly; it has to travel through space to get here, and that takes time.

The Moon is just over 384,000 kilometres away, so it takes a bit more than a second for its reflected light to reach us. Light from the Sun, at 150 million kilometres away, takes over eight minutes, while light from our next closest star, Proxima Centauri travels for four years. When light travels from our neighbouring galaxy, Andromeda, it takes an incredible 2.5 million years to reach us.

This effectively means that looking out into space is the equivalent to looking back in time. The Hubble telescope can see light released by ancient galaxies more than 13 billion years ago.

© NASA, Wiki

How do spacesuits work?

≈✦≈

How this incredible device allows astronauts to survive the extremes

Below
ESA astronaut Alexander Gerst tests his spacesuit at NASA's Johnson Space Center in Houston, Texas

Spacesuits are an astronaut's life support system, providing them with oxygen, keeping them warm and protecting them from the vacuum of space. They provide communications with fellow astronauts and mission control, monitor their health and are sealed against the harsh environment outside. One of the most important parts of any space suit is the backpack: the Primary Life Support System, or PLSS. It's more than just an oxygen pack - it keeps the suit pressurised to prevent hypoxia, removes harmful carbon dioxide and cools the suit by pumping water around it. It also houses medical monitors and the communication equipment.

Inside the suit the astronaut wears a skin-tight Liquid Cooling and Ventilation Garment, which removes body heat through perspiration. Oxygen, carbon dioxide and water vapour are also sent back to the PLSS; the carbon dioxide is then removed by reacting with lithium hydroxide, producing lithium carbonate and water. The water vapour condenses and is also removed and stored in the pack, while oxygen is recycled back around the suit for the astronaut to breathe. If an astronaut on a spacewalk finds themselves drifting off into space, then the modern NASA spacesuits have a device called the Simplified Aid for EVA Rescue, which is composed of little jets that can fly them back to the space station.

∾ *Design details* ∾

An essential piece of clothing for space travel, each part of a spacesuit
has an important job

Helmet with visor
The helmet features a visor
coated with a thin layer of gold to
filter out harmful solar rays.

Build a spacesuit
Spacesuits do not come
in a single piece, but are
built from several pieces
that are fastened
together: the upper
torso, the arms and the
lower torso assemble.

Toilet break
While in the middle of a
spacewalk you can't
just pop to the loo, so a
spacesuit contains a
'maximum absorption
garment' – a fancy
name for a nappy!

Gloves
Space is so cold that
the fingertips in an
astronaut's gloves
contain miniature
heaters. The gloves are
made to be dexterous
while providing a
strong grip.

Life support system
The life support system
contains oxygen tanks as
well as a battery for
power, water-cooling
equipment and a fan for
essential air circulation.

Dexterity
Spacesuits have to
provide astronauts
with a range of motion
for when they are
working outside of the
space station.

Footwear
The boots on current
spacesuits are soft and not
really made for walking, just
floating. New boots will have to
be designed for going back to
the Moon or Mars.

Ventilation garment
The Liquid Cooling and Ventilation
Garment is made from skin-tight
Spandex and worn beneath the space
suit. It contains over 90 metres' worth of
tubing to remove and recycle body heat,
carbon dioxide and perspiration.

© ESA, Getty

Fully equipped office
Towards the front of the hauler is the office area, so the team have somewhere to discuss their race strategies.

Sleeper cab
The front cabin has two beds behind the driver and passenger seats, so that the person who isn't driving can get some well-earned sleep.

Generator
Each hauler has its own generator that provides power for each section, including the office and the parts garage.

Car bay
This level of the transporter holds two race cars, which are loaded using a hydraulic lift gate at the back of the hauler.

What are NASCAR haulers?

How this 18-wheeler transports race cars and more

Over the years NASCAR has become a huge part of American sporting culture. Founded in 1947, it now sanctions more than 1,200 races across America, Canada, Mexico and Europe.

Getting the highly specialised race cars from one race to another presents the teams with a problem. You won't see a race car being driven on normal roads, and since the NASCAR races are so spread out across America, they have to be transported in a specialised hauler to each race venue. They do more than transport cars; they function as repair shops, restaurants, meeting rooms, viewing platforms and storage facilities.

～ *Inside the race shop on wheels* ～

Discover just how much these haulers can store inside them

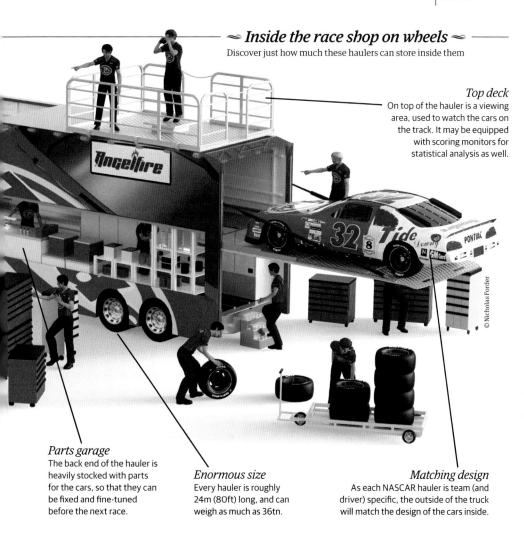

Top deck
On top of the hauler is a viewing area, used to watch the cars on the track. It may be equipped with scoring monitors for statistical analysis as well.

© Nicholas Forder

Parts garage
The back end of the hauler is heavily stocked with parts for the cars, so that they can be fixed and fine-tuned before the next race.

Enormous size
Every hauler is roughly 24m (80ft) long, and can weigh as much as 36tn.

Matching design
As each NASCAR hauler is team (and driver) specific, the outside of the truck will match the design of the cars inside.

As every racetrack on the calendar is different, each NASCAR team will alter the setup of their cars depending on the conditions. This means that every car has to return to the team's base after each race before it can be transported to the next. Once it gets back to base, every single item on board the hauler is removed, before being either cleaned or replaced and then loaded back on. This equates to around 10,000 items – comparable to packing and unpacking a four-bedroom house every week for 38 weeks a year. Without these haulers, the drivers would actually have no feasible way of transporting their cars.

What's inside Boeing's 377 Stratocruiser?

Fly back to the Fifties, where aircraft reached new heights in luxury

Following World War II, cutting-edge military technology was put to commercial use. In the late 1940s, Boeing unveiled the 377 Stratocruiser, an airliner based on the B-29 Superfortress Bomber. The wings had retractable flaps to help minimise drag and allow higher speed, which kept flights as economical as possible.

Four 3,500-horsepower piston engines drove the 377's propellers, helping it reach an altitude of 9,750 metres (32,000 feet). The 377's engines were quite unreliable, due to their complex, 28-cylinder composition. Although designed to fly with only three working engines, this did not save the plane from catastrophe. Between 1951 and 1970, Stratocruisers suffered 13 hull-loss accidents. This is one of the reasons the 377 was retired commercially in favour of jet aircraft.

Post-war air travel

See inside Boeing's first transatlantic commercial plane

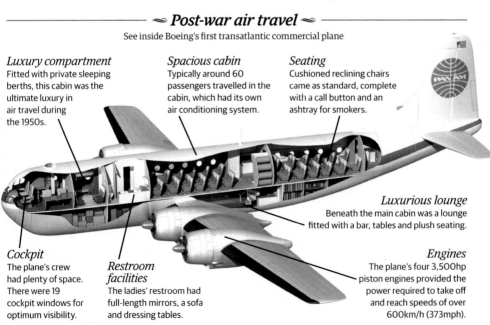

Luxury compartment
Fitted with private sleeping berths, this cabin was the ultimate luxury in air travel during the 1950s.

Spacious cabin
Typically around 60 passengers travelled in the cabin, which had its own air conditioning system.

Seating
Cushioned reclining chairs came as standard, complete with a call button and an ashtray for smokers.

Luxurious lounge
Beneath the main cabin was a lounge fitted with a bar, tables and plush seating.

Cockpit
The plane's crew had plenty of space. There were 19 cockpit windows for optimum visibility.

Restroom facilities
The ladies' restroom had full-length mirrors, a sofa and dressing tables.

Engines
The plane's four 3,500hp piston engines provided the power required to take off and reach speeds of over 600km/h (373mph).

What is the future of VTOL aircrafts?

Meet the fleet that could revolutionise heavy cargo transportation

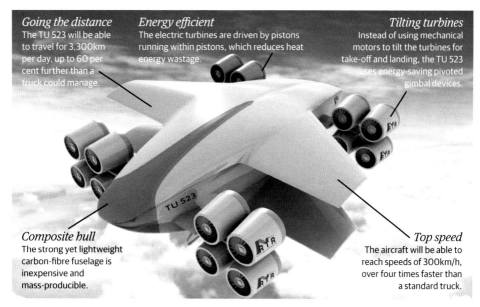

Going the distance
The TU 523 will be able to travel for 3,300km per day, up to 60 per cent further than a truck could manage.

Energy efficient
The electric turbines are driven by pistons running within pistons, which reduces heat energy wastage.

Tilting turbines
Instead of using mechanical motors to tilt the turbines for take-off and landing, the TU 523 uses energy-saving pivoted gimbal devices.

TU 523

Composite hull
The strong yet lightweight carbon-fibre fuselage is inexpensive and mass-producible.

Top speed
The aircraft will be able to reach speeds of 300km/h, over four times faster than a standard truck.

British company Reinhardt Technology Research (RTR) have designed the TU 523, a vertical take-off and landing (VTOL) aircraft, capable of transporting heavy shipping containers without the need for expensive new infrastructure. The craft uses a hybrid electric generator to supply power to a series of electric turbines on demand, which can tilt horizontally and enable vertical take-off and landing.

Once in the air, the turbines automatically tilt back again, while the wings generate lift just like on an airplane. RTR has already built a 1:4 scaled model of the TU 523, which will be sent on a 60-day journey from the UK to South Africa. A full-scale version is then to be developed, which can be mass-produced at a capacity of 30 units per month and cost no more than £400,000 ($580,000) each.

What is the world's largest ship?

How this record-breaking vessel rules the waves

The largest, most monstrous, hands-down winner in the big ships size class is Maersk's Triple E design. Offering 16 per cent more container space due to its wider, bulbous bow.

The engine is also positioned further back to aid stability and allows for yet more containers to be squeezed in above and below deck. The propellers are larger, and move slower to conserve fuel and reduce emissions. The hull is designed to be completely recyclable, while the ship's waste heat recovery system captures the heat and pressure from the exhaust and uses it to move turbines.

The vessel is so enormous it has to be built in a way that can withstand the force of waves, made from flexible materials that can bend with the movement of the ocean. It's possible to see the walls flexing and distorting as the craft moves in heavy swell.

Below
The first Triple E was delivered in July 2013, and was named the Maersk Mc-Kinney Moller

© Juliet Marine Systems

How do GHOST ships work?

The next-gen stealth ship that flies through the waves

Above
GHOST is designed for military use, but can also be adapted for commercial and recreational use

Juliet Marine Systems (JMS) Inc have used innovative technology in the design of its demonstration ship called GHOST. This twin-hull ship has two wing-like struts attached to the main cabin. Instead of being pushed along, front-mounted propellers on each hull pull GHOST through the water. Whereas a conventional propeller vessel leaves a trail of foam in its wake, GHOST's unique design redirects the bubbles to surround the twin hulls with pockets of gas. This effect is known as supercavitation, allowing the boat to glide through air rather than water, which JMS claims can reduce drag by a factor of 900.

GHOST's wings can also be repositioned to lift the main cabin above the bumpy waves. This ensures a smooth ride, protecting the crew from impact injuries and sea sickness, also improving the stability and accuracy of onboard sensors and weapon targeting.

How do wheels work?

Learn about those rubber-wrapped alloys connecting your car to the road

Wheels are one of the most important parts of a car, they are the only parts that connect it to the road. Each wheel is connected to an axle, which rotates on power from the engine. As the axle rotates, so does the wheel, providing motion for a vehicle. The brake system, consisting of a brake disc and a calliper on each wheel, stops the car. The brake disc is attached to the wheel, while the calliper acts as a clamp. When you hit the brake pedal, a piston closes the clamp, slowing the brake disc and stopping the wheel from turning, bringing the vehicle to a halt.

What's inside your car's wheel?

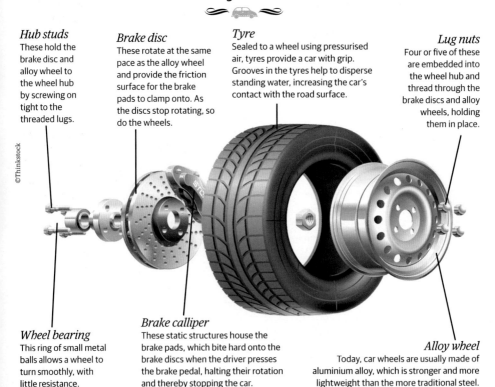

Hub studs
These hold the brake disc and alloy wheel to the wheel hub by screwing on tight to the threaded lugs.

Brake disc
These rotate at the same pace as the alloy wheel and provide the friction surface for the brake pads to clamp onto. As the discs stop rotating, so do the wheels.

Tyre
Sealed to a wheel using pressurised air, tyres provide a car with grip. Grooves in the tyres help to disperse standing water, increasing the car's contact with the road surface.

Lug nuts
Four or five of these are embedded into the wheel hub and thread through the brake discs and alloy wheels, holding them in place.

©Thinkstock

Wheel bearing
This ring of small metal balls allows a wheel to turn smoothly, with little resistance.

Brake calliper
These static structures house the brake pads, which bite hard onto the brake discs when the driver presses the brake pedal, halting their rotation and thereby stopping the car.

Alloy wheel
Today, car wheels are usually made of aluminium alloy, which is stronger and more lightweight than the more traditional steel.

What are airless tyres?

Will Michelin's new airless tyre design end the fight against flat tyres?

Michelin's airless tyre design promises to put an end to frustrating slow punctures and dangerous high-speed blow-outs. Their new 'Tweel' is a combined wheel and tyre assembly in a single, tough unit, primarily designed for commercial use in landscaping, agriculture and construction. If successful, the designers hope to implement the technology in other vehicles.

Solid, air-free tyres have actually existed for quite a while but as they are incredibly hard, the vehicle bounces when travelling over rough terrain. The Michelin Tweel combats this by compressing when it is being driven on rugged roads. Another advantage is that it's much more eco-friendly than current air-filled pneumatic tyres, as it is made of a plastic resin that can be repeatedly recycled. This means that these tyres will have very little environmental impact even when they are replaced.

≈ Inside an airless tyre ≈

See the features that make the Tweel so durable

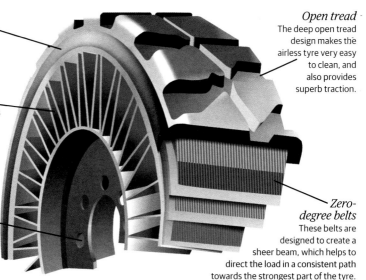

Undertread
A thick undertread means the core of the tyre can be retreaded multiple times.

Strong spokes
The tyre's polyresin spokes help make the ride more comfortable by reducing the amount of bounce when driving.

Great compatibility
Each tyre is fitted with eight-hole steel hub bolts, allowing them to fit all standard skid-steer machines.

Open tread
The deep open tread design makes the airless tyre very easy to clean, and also provides superb traction.

Zero-degree belts
These belts are designed to create a sheer beam, which helps to direct the load in a consistent path towards the strongest part of the tyre.

How do road sweepers work?

~ 🚗 ~

Meet the machines that keep our streets clean

Mechanised road sweepers are like huge vacuum cleaners that suck up everything from leaves and dirt to paper and cans, leaving the roads behind them squeaky clean.

High-pressure water jets break up any caked-in dirt. Rotating 'gutter brooms' sweep this dirt, and any other litter, from the edges of the road into the middle. The sweeper then sprays out a fine mist of water, helping to hold the dust down. The vacuum system is connected to a hose that sits under the centre of the sweeper, it sucks up litter from the road into the vehicle's collection bin.

Once it's in there, the litter is shaken and dried, to break it up into smaller particles, and passed through filters. The dirt is trapped, while the cleaned air is either recycled back into the vacuum system, or released into the environment.

———————— ~ *Sweep me off my street* ~ ————————

Lots of different technologies are used to keep a city's roads clean

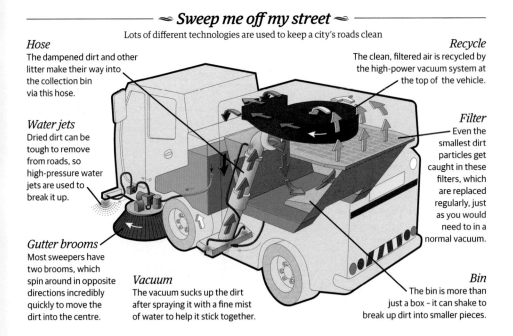

Hose
The dampened dirt and other litter make their way into the collection bin via this hose.

Water jets
Dried dirt can be tough to remove from roads, so high-pressure water jets are used to break it up.

Gutter brooms
Most sweepers have two brooms, which spin around in opposite directions incredibly quickly to move the dirt into the centre.

Vacuum
The vacuum sucks up the dirt after spraying it with a fine mist of water to help it stick together.

Recycle
The clean, filtered air is recycled by the high-power vacuum system at the top of the vehicle.

Filter
Even the smallest dirt particles get caught in these filters, which are replaced regularly, just as you would need to in a normal vacuum.

Bin
The bin is more than just a box – it can shake to break up dirt into smaller pieces.

🚗 *Transport*

Is there a
supersonic jet
without the boom?

Is there a supersonic jet without the boom?

NASA has revealed plans for a quieter successor to the Concorde passenger jet

NASA hope to bring back supersonic passenger air travel by making flights greener, safer and quieter. To achieve this it has announced plans to develop a 'low boom' aircraft, which generates a soft thump as it breaks the sound barrier, rather than a disruptive boom.

The $20 million contract to design the Quiet Supersonic Technology (QueSST) X-plane has been awarded to Lockheed Martin Aeronautics, and NASA hopes a working prototype will take flight in 2020. To help build this next-generation supersonic jet, NASA has been busy conducting research into sonic booms. It has recently been testing an air data probe that may one day be used to measure the shockwaves generated by supersonic aircraft.

Below
An artist's concept of a possible design for the Low Boom QueSST X-plane

Low drag
Triangular 'delta' wings help to reduce drag, making supersonic flight possible.

Elongated nose
A narrow point at the nose of the plane will help to reduce the force of the shockwaves it produces.

Video view
One QueSST concept eliminates the forward-facing cockpit window. Pilots would navigate with help from video cameras.

©NASA

How do aerodynamics work?

How the shape of a vehicle can help it slip through the air

As a car moves through the air it pushes aside air molecules, which creates a resistant force called drag. The faster a car travels, the greater the drag, meaning the car's engine has to work even harder to maintain speed. As car speeds have increased, it has become more important for drag to be kept to a minimum - that's where aerodynamics come into play. Ensuring a car has good aerodynamics means giving it a more chiselled appearance from the front, reducing its surface area that will come into contact with the air.

Enhancing the flow of air around a car not only reduces drag, making it more economical, but also allows it to slip through the atmosphere quicker, making it faster. Airflow is also utilised to keep key parts of the car cool, such as the engine and brakes, to maintain its performance even under sustained heavy use.

Using airflow to go faster

How a sports car is designed for improved performance

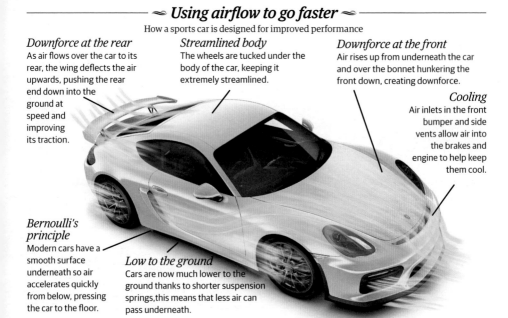

Downforce at the rear
As air flows over the car to its rear, the wing deflects the air upwards, pushing the rear end down into the ground at speed and improving its traction.

Streamlined body
The wheels are tucked under the body of the car, keeping it extremely streamlined.

Downforce at the front
Air rises up from underneath the car and over the bonnet hunkering the front down, creating downforce.

Cooling
Air inlets in the front bumper and side vents allow air into the brakes and engine to help keep them cool.

Bernoulli's principle
Modern cars have a smooth surface underneath so air accelerates quickly from below, pressing the car to the floor.

Low to the ground
Cars are now much lower to the ground thanks to shorter suspension springs,this means that less air can pass underneath.

∾ *Riding in comfort* ∾
A crash course in how air con works

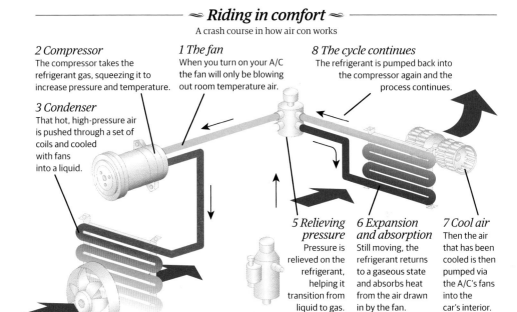

2 Compressor
The compressor takes the refrigerant gas, squeezing it to increase pressure and temperature.

3 Condenser
That hot, high-pressure air is pushed through a set of coils and cooled with fans into a liquid.

1 The fan
When you turn on your A/C the fan will only be blowing out room temperature air.

8 The cycle continues
The refrigerant is pumped back into the compressor again and the process continues.

5 Relieving pressure
Pressure is relieved on the refrigerant, helping it transition from liquid to gas.

6 Expansion and absorption
Still moving, the refrigerant returns to a gaseous state and absorbs heat from the air drawn in by the fan.

7 Cool air
Then the air that has been cooled is then pumped via the A/C's fans into the car's interior.

4 Filtering
The receiver then cleans the refrigerant of ice crystals and impurities before it's pushed into the expansion valve.

What is inside your car's air con?

The subtle engineering that is sure to keep you cool behind the wheel

It all starts when you press the A/C button on your dashboard. Firstly, a refrigerant gas (usually Puron or Freon) is pumped through a series of tubes by a compressor. The compressor forces the vapour into a high-pressure state, causing its temperature to rise.

This hot air passes through a condenser, which uses fans to cool the refrigerant gas into a liquid. The cool liquid is then pumped into a receiver, which removes any moisture

or ice crystals that could damage the circuit. Finally, it is pumped into an expansion valve that reduces its overall pressure, allowing it to pass into the evaporator.

The refrigerant has a very low boiling point and so becomes a gas again, even at the temperature of the car cabin. Heat from the air drawn in by the fans on the dashboard is then absorbed by the refrigerant, and the cool air that remains is pumped into the car's interior.

How are torpedoes fired?

Learn how to unleash the ultimate underwater weapon

≈ Load, aim and fire! ≈
How to fire a torpedo during battle

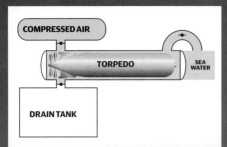

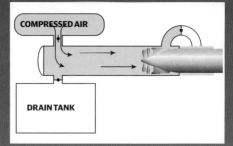

1 Load your weapon
Load the torpedo through the breech door at the back of the torpedo tube and then close it. Open the valve to flood the tube with seawater from outside the ship, equalising the pressure inside and outside the tube.

2 Fire!
Open the muzzle door at the front of the torpedo tube, open the compressed air valve to eject the torpedo. The air is vented into the ship, so that a bubble cannot escape to the surface and give away the ship's position.

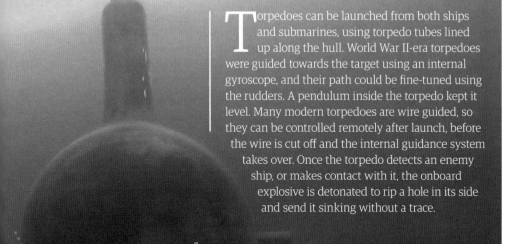

Torpedoes can be launched from both ships and submarines, using torpedo tubes lined up along the hull. World War II-era torpedoes were guided towards the target using an internal gyroscope, and their path could be fine-tuned using the rudders. A pendulum inside the torpedo kept it level. Many modern torpedoes are wire guided, so they can be controlled remotely after launch, before the wire is cut off and the internal guidance system takes over. Once the torpedo detects an enemy ship, or makes contact with it, the onboard explosive is detonated to rip a hole in its side and send it sinking without a trace.

Above
Torpedoes are fired from
ships and submarines
through torpedo tubes

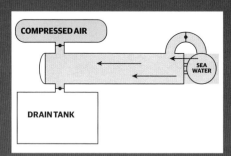

3 Maintain balance
Shut off the compressed air valve and the torpedo tube will then fill with seawater through the open muzzle door. This will help to offset the lost weight of the torpedo to keep the ship balanced.

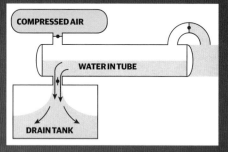

4 Reset and repeat
Shut the muzzle door and open the valve to the drain tank to empty the water from the torpedo tube. Once it is empty, you can then open the breech door and load another torpedo to start the process again.

How do we get real-time traffic data?

How modern sat navs keep you up to date with the latest traffic news

When sat navs first came onto the market they functioned only to get you from one place to another. Modern varieties now offer live traffic data, to keep you aware of developments on the roads as they happen in real time.

The bulk of this information is actually provided by the drivers' journeys as they're undertaken. A small mobile device, similar to a SIM card, is built into the sat nav, which sends data on the speed it's travelling at and its precise geographical location back to the manufacturer's headquarters.

Along with this data, live information is gathered from mobile phone networks, radio reports and government organisations, which have access to traffic data through a multitude of cameras and road sensors. These detect the volume and speed of vehicles, using either radar or active infrared, and then wirelessly transmit the results to a server. By combining these various data sources, it's possible to show where the most congestion is and where traffic is still flowing freely.

Live traffic data can also be used to create faster, alternative routes for drivers who are already part way through their journey. Once these have been compiled they are sent directly to sat nav systems; drivers can then choose to change their route to save some time or continue on their original path.

Below
Live traffic data can be used to offer alternative routes to delayed drivers

What is countersteering?

Why motorcyclists must steer in the opposite direction to turn corners

When taking a corner, a motorcyclist will momentarily steer in the opposite direction to where they want to go. This is known as countersteering, and is a safer way of turning at high speeds.

To turn left, you start by pushing gently on the left-hand grip, which turns the front wheel to the right. This positions the wheels for a right-hand turn but as you are going from a straight direction of travel, this turn is unstable. The friction created between the wheels and the ground causes the bike to tilt the other way. This leans you and the bike to the left, setting it up for a left turn instead.

Once you've released the pressure on the left-hand grip, the bike will perform a safe, stable, left-hand turn. The amount you lean is very important - taking a turn incorrectly can lead to severe injury.

～ *Mastering the turn* ～

How do riders balance out forces to keep their bike from falling?

Angular momentum
As a rolling wheel has both forward and angular momentum, it will maintain its speed and angle unless forced to do otherwise.

Gravity
Too much lean will cause the bike to fall to the ground, as gravity will overcome centripetal force.

Balanced forces
For the bike to remain upright, the forces pulling it into the turn and out of it need to be balanced.

Centripetal force
Created by friction between the wheels and the ground, this force tips the bike in the direction you want to turn.

How does the Super Yacht Sub work?

❤❦❤

Explore life beneath the waves in this luxury submarine

The Super Yacht Sub 3 (SYS3) is a personal submersible, costing a bank-breaking £1.6 million ($2.4 million), that gives three passengers the opportunity to explore 300 metres below the ocean's surface.

Four electric thrusters propel the SYS3. Two mounted at the rear of the sub, while the other two are on the side, allowing movement in any direction. The power comes from a lithium-ion battery, which provides 21.6 kilowatt-hours to the thrusters and onboard operating systems. Enabling the sub to reach a top speed of 2.8 knots (just over five kilometres per hour), both underwater and on the surface.

The submarine is steered using a dual-joystick controller featuring a 'dead man's switch', which must be pressed every ten minutes to prevent the sub from returning to the surface.

❤ *Exploring the oceans* ❤

See the features that help the submarine to function underwater

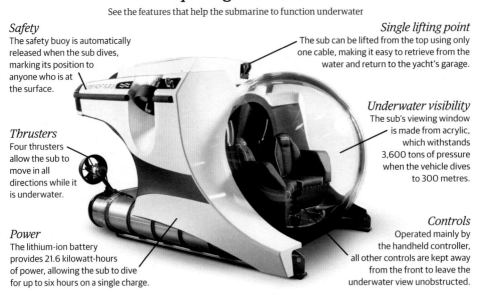

Safety
The safety buoy is automatically released when the sub dives, marking its position to anyone who is at the surface.

Single lifting point
The sub can be lifted from the top using only one cable, making it easy to retrieve from the water and return to the yacht's garage.

Underwater visibility
The sub's viewing window is made from acrylic, which withstands 3,600 tons of pressure when the vehicle dives to 300 metres.

Thrusters
Four thrusters allow the sub to move in all directions while it is underwater.

Power
The lithium-ion battery provides 21.6 kilowatt-hours of power, allowing the sub to dive for up to six hours on a single charge.

Controls
Operated mainly by the handheld controller, all other controls are kept away from the front to leave the underwater view unobstructed.

The bridge is the longest sea crossing in Southeast Asia

What is a disaster-resistant bridge?

Malaysia's new 24-kilometre bridge can withstand tsunamis and earthquakes

Above
In an area prone to natural disaster, the Second Penang Bridge will save lives

Few man-made structures can survive the unforgiving wrath of Mother Nature, but the Second Penang Bridge in Malaysia can lay claim to just that. Innovative technology used in the construction means it is both earthquake and tsunami-resistant. The bridge is rooted into position by a series of wide, pre-cast concrete pylons mounted at a world record depth of 127 metres (417 feet). Cables are connected to the pylons using third-generation saddles, improving their hold. The 24-kilometre (14.9-mile) bridge has a curved appearance when viewed from above. This is to reduce traffic accidents, forcing drivers to reduce their speed and concentrate on the curve of the road.

Can aviation be eco-friendly?

The future of aviation is designed to be lightweight, cleaner and quieter

When it comes to reinvention of light passenger aircraft, there are few more innovative than the Bio-Electric-Hybrid-Aircraft (BEHA).

Seeking to lower costs while offering safer operational capability with lower noise and emissions the BEHA has three engines on board, with one bio-diesel engine effectively powering two electric motors - though the plane can be flown purely on the bio-diesel reserve engine. This improves its safety in the event of engine failure. Solar skin panels will ensure greater energy generation and recovery during flight, in a bid to reduce emissions.

What's more, the plane can take off and land on pure electric energy for reduced flight noise, ensuring it can be used around the clock, even in urban areas where night restrictions may apply. It's not just the plane's power source that breaks with tradition, either. Made entirely from carbon fibre BEHA is designed to be lightweight yet strong.

Lift-off won't be for a while yet, as the prototype is still in development, but the sky's the limit according to Faradair.

Power
A bio-diesel engine creates power for the generator of two electric motors, though each can be used on its own to offer three different engine reserves for the hybrid craft.

Enhanced safety
If all three engines fail, the plane has excellent glide capabilities, but if that's not good enough, BEHA will be fitted with a ballistic parachute recovery system.

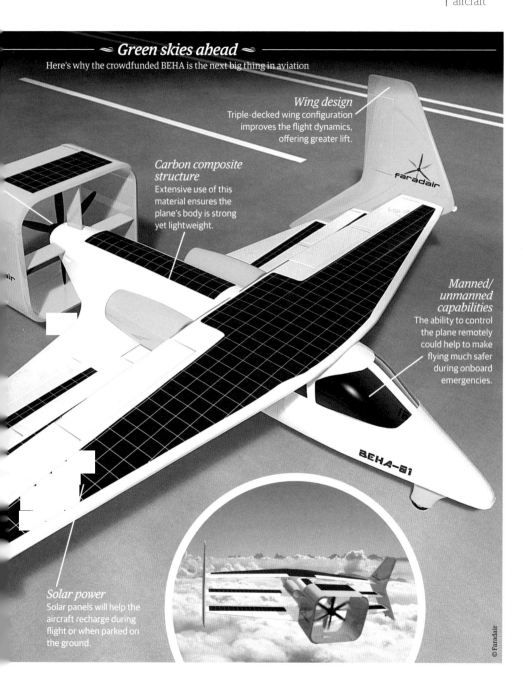

≈ *Green skies ahead* ≈

Here's why the crowdfunded BEHA is the next big thing in aviation

Wing design
Triple-decked wing configuration improves the flight dynamics, offering greater lift.

Carbon composite structure
Extensive use of this material ensures the plane's body is strong yet lightweight.

Manned/ unmanned capabilities
The ability to control the plane remotely could help to make flying much safer during onboard emergencies.

Solar power
Solar panels will help the aircraft recharge during flight or when parked on the ground.

faradair

BEHA-01

© Faradair

How did the Romans deal with crime and punishment?

Hold on to your coin purse and take a trip down the mean streets of ancient Rome

Below
The Praetorian Guard was very influential and played a role in the removal and accession of several different emperors

During the first century CE it is estimated that the city of Rome supported 1 million inhabitants. As with any city, densely populated areas with wide class divides can easily become criminal hotspots. The foundation of Roman law was known as the Twelve Tables, a dozen rules that every citizen had to obey. The Twelve Tables were so important that schoolchildren learnt to read and write by copying laws down and reciting them. While some soldiers, volunteers and officials were tasked with keeping the peace, the city had no dedicated police force, so upholding the law could be difficult. Harsh punishments were the main deterrents, ranging from a brutal beheading to elaborate public executions at the Colosseum. The crimes committed and punishments received often depended on the social standing of the accused. High-class citizens convicted of major crimes were often given the option of exile rather than execution. Slaves, on the other hand, were punished harshly. If one slave was caught committing a crime, it was not uncommon for all the other slaves of the household to actually be punished as well, this was in order to try and discourage any possible uprisings.

≈ *Keeping the peace* ≈

While there was no official police force in Ancient Rome, leaders enlisted some groups to be in charge of crime prevention. Vigiles were volunteers who performed the dual role of police and firefighters. They patrolled the city at night, scouting for potential criminals or runaway slaves, while also helping to extinguish fires. Urban cohorts were soldiers that played the role of riot police. Rather than patrolling the streets, only summoned if a situation got out of hand.

The Praetorian Guard was responsible for protecting the Emperor, just like bodyguards. Despite only having a single person to protect, at times the Praetorian Guard actually consisted of over 1,000 men. None of these groups were tasked with catching criminals after a crime was committed. If Roman citizens were victims of crime, it was actually their responsibility to catch the perpetrator and then take him or her to the magistrate for a trial.

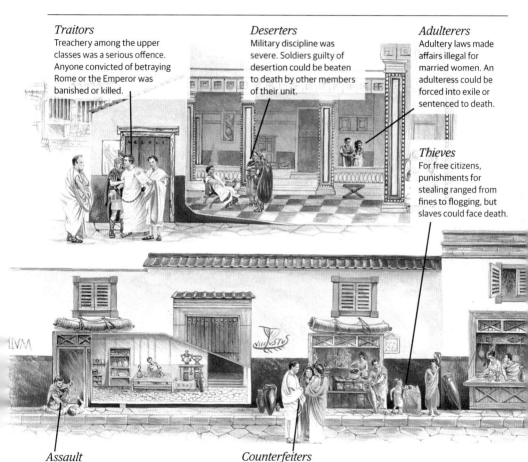

Traitors
Treachery among the upper classes was a serious offence. Anyone convicted of betraying Rome or the Emperor was banished or killed.

Deserters
Military discipline was severe. Soldiers guilty of desertion could be beaten to death by other members of their unit.

Adulterers
Adultery laws made affairs illegal for married women. An adulteress could be forced into exile or sentenced to death.

Thieves
For free citizens, punishments for stealing ranged from fines to flogging, but slaves could face death.

Assault
One of the Twelve Tables stated that anybody who broke another's limb should receive punishment in kind.

Counterfeiters
One of the Twelve Tables stated that anybody who broke another's limb should receive punishment in kind.

© Wiki

What were the secrets to Tudor beauty?

The dos and don'ts of looking gorgeous in 16th century England

Below
Anne Boleyn wasn't considered beautiful, due to her dark hair and sallow skin

Perception of beauty varies greatly throughout history, and the Tudors went to great lengths to achieve the ideal.

Pale skin was a sign of wealth and relaxation, and tanned, or sunburned skin was an indication of hard labour. Women softened their skin with creams and ointments, and even used ceruse, a cream made of white lead and vinegar, to whiten their complexion. Many suffered from lead poisoning as a result, but they also went to further extremes, such as bleeding themselves to remove any rosy flush.

Darker-haired ladies dyed their locks red with henna, or tried to lighten it using urine or cumin, saffron seeds, celandine and oil. Wigs were also fashionable, and high-class women would wear these to achieve the desired colour without a messy dye job.

≈ *The model queen* ≈

The Darnley Portrait of Elizabeth I was completed circa 1575 and shows her as a picture of popular beauty

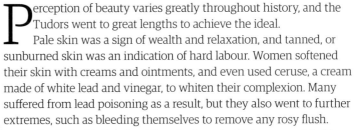

High hairline
Ladies would pluck their hairline to achieve a higher forehead, and heavily arch their eyebrows.

Light hair
A Tudor ideal was fair hair – either blonde or red. Wigs were very popular.

Pale complexion
During Elizabeth I's reign women painted their faces with ceruse.

Soft skin
During Henry VIII's reign, women used cream containing beeswax and honey for soft, dewy skin.

Red cheeks and lips
Tudor ladies used mercuric sulphide on their cheeks and lips for a bright vermillion colour and blush.

©Thinkstock, Wiki

Who were Africa's witch doctors?

The truth behind the so-called spiritual healers

African witch doctors have been practising for around 5,000 years, and are neither witches nor doctors. Their roles and titles vary between regions and tribes but these folk healers often act as either a herbalist, a diviner, or both. They were and still are very highly respected members of society, whose aim is to cure the sick and keep evil spirits away with the help of various different potions and traditions.

However, scientists hope to learn more about the effectiveness of the traditional medicines used by these healers, as they have not been well-studied. Some believe it is possible that certain herbal remedies may be beneficial in the treatment of HIV symptoms.

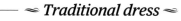

⟿ Traditional dress ⟿

With vibrant headwear and facial piercings, witch doctors were both feared and respected

Face paint
The witch doctor's face paint had hidden meaning; circles around the eyes indicated the ability to see hidden sickness and evil.

Facial piercing
Large facial piercings signified status, and were also traditional throughout most of the world's tribal civilisations.

Below
Depending on the type of procedure they're performing, witch doctors will sometimes wear a mask

Headdress
Made from a range of feathers, teeth and even animal skins, the headdress was designed to impress and intimidate.

Loincloth
Not just to keep their dignity, the loincloth was a key part of the witch doctor's traditional dress, often containing a medicine pouch.

Staff
This simple tool was ideal for mixing herbal remedies or drawing in the dirt.

Nkondi
These small wooden statues were used by the Kongo people. They were believed to house a spirit that could hunt down enemies.

~ *101 Amazing Facts You Need To Know*

What was it
like to be an
American GI?

What was it like to be an American GI?

The Vietnam War saw huge changes in uniform regulations

Alightweight, wind-resistant material called poplin was used to keep soldiers cool in the blistering Sun. This fabric also featured a threaded grid design that prevented it from ripping, while drawstrings around the trousers helped to keep creepy crawlies out. Hybrid boots were introduced, consisting of a leather bottom half and quick-drying canvas on the sides.

ERDL camouflage, which is a mixture of shapes coloured either brown, green, beige or black which blend extremely well with the jungle environment, was also introduced to their uniform.

Many of these different innovations, along with the introduction of the M16 rifle, became a vital part to the soldiers who served in the Vietnam War.

~ *Jungle combat* ~

How US Army soldiers were equipped to fight
through the challenging conditions

M1 helmet
Standard US Army issue since WWII, troops often customised their helmets with peace signs or playing cards

Armour
The soldier's zip-up flak vests provided protection and a means of storing ammunition and grenades.

Utility belt
Fitted with a canteen and extra ammunition, these belts were heavy and cumbersome, but carried vital supplies.

M16 rifle
Replacing the heavy M14, this rifle was lightweight and produced a high rate of fire.

Boots
A leather and canvas boots enabled the feet to breathe and water to escape through drainage eyelets.

Smoke grenades
The coloured smoke was used to provide cover, mark landing zones and identify the location of casualties.

Combat clothing
Made of tightly woven fabric, the olive-green clothing provided camouflage and protection from all weathers.

History

What was life like
inside a Victorian
household?

What was life like inside a Victorian household?

Discover how the middle classes lived in 19th century Britain

Middle class homes were typically large terraced houses, with front and back gardens and plenty of room for their wife, children and a few servants to live comfortably. Most homes had at least one maid, one cook and a gardener. The family provided the servants with clothing, food and living quarters, and in return they would be required to work long hours for a meagre wage.

Managing the staff was often the job of the lady of the house, who spent most of their time was spent entertaining guests, shopping and attending social engagements, while a governess looked after their children for them.

⁓ *Grand designs* ⁓

Take a tour of a traditional terraced house

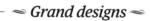
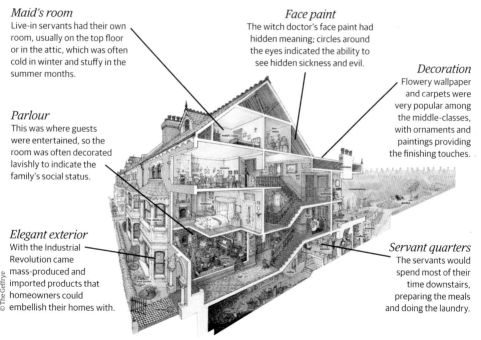

Maid's room
Live-in servants had their own room, usually on the top floor or in the attic, which was often cold in winter and stuffy in the summer months.

Face paint
The witch doctor's face paint had hidden meaning; circles around the eyes indicated the ability to see hidden sickness and evil.

Decoration
Flowery wallpaper and carpets were very popular among the middle-classes, with ornaments and paintings providing the finishing touches.

Parlour
This was where guests were entertained, so the room was often decorated lavishly to indicate the family's social status.

Elegant exterior
With the Industrial Revolution came mass-produced and imported products that homeowners could embellish their homes with.

Servant quarters
The servants would spend most of their time downstairs, preparing the meals and doing the laundry.

© The Geffrye

Why was the Ancient Greek theatre so popular?

Uncover the civilisation that invented the play and set the stage for Western culture

We have a lot to thank Ancient Greece for. From democracy to philosophy, this thriving collection of city-states was the birthplace of so many things that we take for granted today - including theatre.

The first mention of it dates back to 532 BCE, when an actor called Thespis performed a tragedy. His name has been immortalised as a term for a performer - a 'thespian'. A few decades later, a festival called the City Dionysia was established in Athens to honour Dionysus, the god of wine. The events centred on competitive performances of tragedies and, from 487 BCE, comedies. Thousands flocked from all over Greece, businesses closed and prisoners were released to take part in five days of festivities. Performances were staged at the Theatre of Dionysus, considered by many to be the first ever built. This was a huge open-air arena that could seat up to 17,000 people on rows of benches set into a hill. The actors performed in the centre, known as the 'orchestra', while a backdrop was painted onto a building behind the stage known as the 'skene'. This was also where the actors changed into their masks and costumes.

The theatre's acoustics were so well thought out that every single audience member would have been able to hear the actors performing, even in the days before microphones and sound systems. Over two thousand years later, we still base our theatre designs on these incredible ancient structures.

Below
The ruins of the theatre of Dionysus as they appear today

∽ *How to put on a play in Ancient Greece* ∽

Follow these steps to produce your very own dramatic masterpiece

1. Pick a genre

In Ancient Greece, tragedy and comedy should never mix. The City Dionysia pits the writers of these two genres against each other in its annual theatre competition, so choose a side and get planning.

2. Get funding

Plays in Athens are publicly funded, but you will need to pitch your idea to an official, who is known as the eponymous archon, and get his approval, before you see the colour of his money.

3. Decide your actors

The eponymous archon is responsible for deciding your lead actors, which is done by drawing random lots. The chorus actors are paid for by wealthy citizens looking to win public favour.

4. Start writing

Not only do your plays have to be written in verse, you'll also need to make sure you compose the music to accompany them. As for subject matter, the more revolutionary the better.

5. Perform your play

Once rehearsals are over, it's then time to bring your work to the big stage. The competitions can attract up to a staggering 17,000 people and can even last from dawn until dusk.

6. Collect your prize

The judges will then write their scores on tablets and place them in urns. The eponymous archon draws five of them at random and the winner is awarded with a wreath and a goat!

What was life like for a Victorian maid?

Discover the daily toils and troubles of a 19th century housemaid

In the large country homes and townhouses of Victorian Britain, it was a maid's job to be unseen and certainly not heard. That wasn't always easy when there was work to be done in every room of the house, and with gruelling shifts that were often 16 hours long. From the crack of dawn until the last drop of port had been drunk, a housemaid's day was filled with lots of cleaning and clearing, serving and sweeping.

Without modern-day appliances like vacuums and dishwashers to help them, this was no mean feat. Many suffered from ailments like 'prepatellar bursitis', an inflammation of the knee, caused by many hours spent scrubbing floors. Despite this, they considered themselves lucky to have a roof over their head, let alone a job. After all, sore knees were nothing compared to the horrors of the workhouse.

Maids were often recruited as young as eight years old and many came from the country, as they were considered more adaptable and harder working than children from the cities. A housemaid, who was responsible for general jobs around the house, earned about £16 a year - equivalent to a measly £960 ($1,370) today. On the plus side this included everything from board, lodging and all of their clothes, and when you were working seven days a week, there was very little time to spend money anyway. The work varied depending on the size of the household and how many servants there were. Each day had a strict routine, and there wasn't a single minute when there wasn't work to be done.

~ The daily routine ~

A Victorian maid's schedule was a never-ending list of chores

06:00 *Wake up*
Our maid wakes and quickly dresses. Her uniform is a simple black dress, a pinafore and a cap.

06:30 *Light the fires*
The carpets are swept and the fireplaces cleaned before new fires are lit. The family are then woken.

08:30 *Serve breakfast*
After eating her porridge, the maid brings out breakfast for the family. This often includes eggs, sausages and kippers.

10:30 *Make the beds*
After clearing the breakfast table, it's time to clean the family bedrooms, make the beds and scrub down the bathrooms.

12:00 *Eat lunch*
The servants have their main meal at midday. It's usually a simple dish of meat and potatoes and a boiled pudding.

14:00 *Clean silver*
Once the family has eaten a three-course lunch, the table is then cleared, the dishes washed, and the silver polished.

16:30 *Serve tea*
Our maid has barely finished clearing up after lunch when the bell rings for afternoon tea.

18:00 *Prepare dinner*
The family eats dinner at 20:00, but before then there are vegetables to be chopped and a table to be laid.

22:30 *Bedtime*
When the dishes are washed, and after a quick supper of bread and cheese, it's finally time for bed.

How has beer changed?

The history of the world's most widely consumed alcoholic tipple

1988
Plastic Widgets

Invented originally for Guinness, plastic widgets are nitrogen-filled spheres. Now common in many lightly carbonated beers, they help release some of the dissolved carbon dioxide bubbles when pouring, creating a frothy 'head'.

1933
Beer can

The Gottfried Krueger Brewing Company was the first to produce beer cans, initially creating 2,000 which were given to its customers to trial. The original aluminium design weighed roughly seven times the average beer can today..

1858
Fermentation

The French chemist Louis Pasteur demonstrated that yeast was responsible for fermenting sugar into alcohol. He also showed that bacterial life could spoil beer, and invented a method called pasteurisation that killed microbes with heat.

Circa 1500
Growing popularity

During the Middle Ages, beer became hugely popular, particularly in Europe. In 1516 Germany introduced the first purity law, stating that beer may only be brewed from water, hops and barley.

Circa 800
Hops

The first written evidence of hops being used as a beer ingredient is from a French monastery. By the 13th century they were used as a preservative, replacing traditional mixes of herbs and spices, and imparting a bitter, tangy flavour.

Circa 9000-7000 BCE
Barley

Although beer's true origins are unknown, many believe it was invented by accident during the Neolithic era. Wild yeast may have settled on barley that had germinated, starting the fermentation process and creating alcohol.

Who were the Mexican bandits?

Meet the outlaws who fought in the Mexican Revolution

Below
*Pancho Villa (centre)
dressed for battle
with his
revolutionaries*

© WIKI

In 1910 Francisco Madero dared to challenge Díaz for power and the president had him jailed. However, Madero escaped from prison and called for his followers to revolt against the government. Armies of revolutionaries began to spring up across the country.

These gangs of bandits used all the firepower they could get their hands on to steal from the rich and give to the poor. They managed to successfully oust Díaz in 1911 but this didn't end the political unrest.

Madero was soon overthrown by Victoriano Huerta, who turned out to be even worse than Díaz, Groups began to turn on each other and even against the US, resulting in many bloody conflicts. Several leaders later, the revolution came to a close, but the legend of the Mexican bandits lives on to this day.

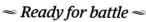

～ *Ready for battle* ～

The essential kit for Mexican
revolutionaries

Bandolier
This long sash had several pockets for holding ammunition, ensuring it was always within easy reach for quick reloading.

Fiat money
Bandits began printing their own paper money to fund their cause. It was accepted as currency in the US all throughout the revolution.

Sombrero
Large hats helped to shield the bandits' eyes from the intense Mexican sun so that their view of the enemy wasn't ever obstructed.

Weapons
The bandits would use whatever arms they could get their hands on, with rifles proving a popular choice.

Horse
Travelling on horseback allowed for a speedy getaway and helped make the troops more mobile.

© Wiki

How were vinyl records made?

Take a spin around this retro method of mass-producing music

As the vinyl disc spins on the record player, a needle - or stylus - moves along the grooves on its surface. It vibrates as it traces over the thousands of tiny bumps and the music plays. The tech seems simple compared to an iPod or a wireless speaker, yet the process to make one of these vinyl records is quite intricate.

Once engineers had perfected the recording in the studio, they would create a master disc. This was made of aluminium and coated with a black lacquer. A machine equipped with an electronic cutting stylus, or needle, would etch the grooves into the lacquer, its path directed by electrical signals from the audio. The finished record was coated with a layer of metal, such as silver or nickel, and this so-called master would form the mould for all the records that would be produced. Liquid nickel was poured into the cast to create a 'stamping record' - a negative version of the record with ridges instead of grooves - and this was connected to a hydraulic press and used to directly print into the vinyl. The stamping record would be lowered onto the vinyl (which was softened by heating with steam) to squeeze it into its final shape and imprint the audio. The disc was then removed, hardened in a water bath, and cut to size using a sharp blade.

Before the records could be sold, a handful were inspected for sound quality. Flawed copies were melted and pressed again.

Below
Thomas Edison pictured with one of his early phonographs, circa 1878

≈ Making a hit record ≈

From the studio to your turntable

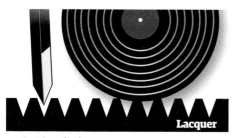

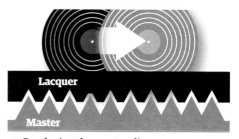

1 *Cutting the lacquer*
Tiny grooves were etched into the lacquered discs by a record-cutting machine's needle. This was guided by the audio of the specific song.

2 *Producing the master disc*
The lacquer was not tough enough for the production process, so was coated with silver or nickel. It was then peeled off and discarded, leaving the metal master.

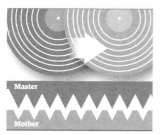

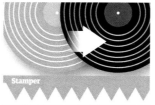

3 *Creating the 'mother'*
The master was re-cut once more to make a mother record. This was then replated to create the 'stamper', which could then be used to mass produce the record.

4 *Stamping the vinyl*
A fresh piece of vinyl was sandwiched between the stamper and a hydraulic press. Steam was used to soften the vinyl, enabling the stamper to imprint it with grooves.

5 *Quality control*
Before the finished vinyl could be sent to shops, a few were played in order to check that they were working correctly and that there were no imperfections.

≈ Thomas Edison's phonograph ≈

The inventor of the electric light bulb and the motion picture camera was also the grandfather of modern record players. In 1877 Thomas Edison and his assistants were working on a way to record telegraph messages using paper strips wrapped around rollers. He attached a needle to the diaphragm in a telephone mouthpiece, which vibrated with sound energy when someone spoke, creating squiggles on the paper. Once the sound was recorded in this way, it could be replayed by rotating the cylinder in the opposite direction, which dragged a second needle backwards through the indentations the first had made. Edison and his team produced a working prototype, recording their own rendition of Mary Had A Little Lamb.

Within six months, Edison had replaced the paper strips with tinfoil to improve the sound quality, and the first phonograph was born. Edison's work paved the way for other inventors to refine and improve the recording process, which eventually led to the record player and vinyl records.

© Wiki

What was WWI's Vickers-Maxim gun?

Stare down the barrel of this deadly British weapon

The Vickers-Maxim machine gun obliterated battlefields, rattling off over 450 rounds a minute. It entered service in time to see action during World War I and served the British Army for more than 50 years.

The key to the design was that it used the power of the cartridge explosion to reload and re-cock the gun after each shot. This became known as a recoil system, as the forward force of the bullet produced an opposing force - the recoil. The force generated pushed the bolt and barrel backwards, while they were locked together. A small metal catch then unlocked the two parts as they moved backwards, before the spring pushed the barrel forward again. The backward motion also ejected the used shell, and a new cartridge was automatically loaded into place from the ammunition belt. If the trigger was still depressed, the whole cycle started again and another shot would fire almost immediately. Although the Vickers was rather heavy and required a team of six to operate, it was extremely reliable. During a British attack in 1916, it's estimated that ten Vickers fired more than one million rounds in just 12 hours

~ *Ready, aim, fire!* ~

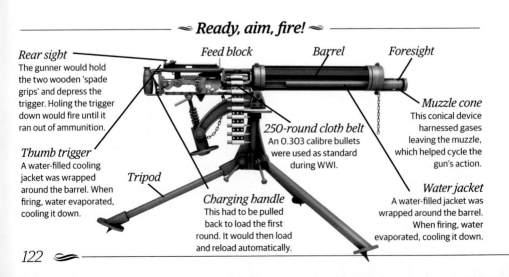

Rear sight
The gunner would hold the two wooden 'spade grips' and depress the trigger. Holing the trigger down would fire until it ran out of ammunition.

Feed block

Barrel

Foresight

Muzzle cone
This conical device harnessed gases leaving the muzzle, which helped cycle the gun's action.

Thumb trigger
A water-filled cooling jacket was wrapped around the barrel. When firing, water evaporated, cooling it down.

Tripod

250-round cloth belt
An 0.303 calibre bullets were used as standard during WWI.

Charging handle
This had to be pulled back to load the first round. It would then load and reload automatically.

Water jacket
A water-filled jacket was wrapped around the barrel. When firing, water evaporated, cooling it down.

How were Anderson shelters built?

These shelters protected millions during WWII

The Anderson shelter was designed to protect up to six people from bombings, and was made of curved, corrugated steel sheets. A shallow pit was dug in the ground, then the six steel sides were put in place and bolted together. The shelter's roof was covered in a thick layer of earth. By the end of World War II, more than 3.5 million of these structures had been erected throughout the UK.

Due to their corrugation, these shelters stood up to nearby bomb blasts surprisingly well. The explosive force of a bomb would easily buckle flat metal sheets, but the curved structure of corrugated steel absorbed this energy without sustaining a huge amount of damage.

To prevent the shelters from rusting, their steel sides were coated in zinc, a process known as galvanisation. Zinc reacts more readily with oxygen, which means it rusts instead of the iron and the shelter's walls remain intact. As a result, some Anderson shelters are still standing, over 70 years after the end of the war.

∼ *Inside the safe haven* ∼

See the design that withstood the Blitz attacks

Protective cover
Travelling on horseback allowed for a speedy getaway and helped make the troops more mobile.

Iron panels
Six corrugated steel sheets were bolted together to form the shelter's walls, with steel plates at either end.

Cramped conditions
Six people were expected to pile into a single shelter, which left little room once the air raids began.

Self-assembly
Supplied with only a flat pack kit, families had to build the shelters themselves.

Were there drones in WWII?

How UAVs first took to the skies over 70 years ago

In 1933, a modified floatplane called Fairey Queen was tested as the first ever flightless drone aircraft. It crashed on two out of three trials, but in 1934, Queen Bee, a modified Tiger Moth aircraft, followed with greater success.

Training gunners on these rudimentary models wasn't a very realistic simulation, but a solution was soon to come from the United States in the form of British-born actor Reginald Denny, and his Radioplane Company. After years of trying desperately to interest the US Navy in the Radioplane-1, Denny succeeded in 1939 and over the course of the war some 15,374 models of Radioplane were built.

Fast, agile and durable, fitted with responsive radio control and were able to mimic the speed and agility of the enemy's fighters.

～ *Beneath the hood of the first UAVs* ～

Empty cockpit
The cockpit housed a pump in the rear which drove the pneumatic actuators.

Steering trouble
The ailerons were locked in a neutral position and the pilot had to steer using only the rudder.

Spread your wings
A larger dihedral made the plane more stable. It crashed four times out of five.

Remote control
A rotary dial like that on an old telephone transmitted commands by radio signal.

How did we measure ocean depth?

Meet the man responsible for the first modern flushing toilet

Below
Sounding lines were tossed overboard to measure the depth of the ocean

Egyptions were the first to attempt to measure the depth of the oceans as shown by paintings from 1800 BCE. The images show a man on a boat dipping a sounding pole into the water, measuring how far it goes before it reaches the bottom.

Measurements were taken in shallow areas, identifying near-shore hazards. In 1872 the first wide-scale study of the oceans began. The HMS Challenger took 360 depth readings of the sea floor. The devices used a weight to pull a sounding line to the seafloor, collecting samples from the seabed in the process. Helping to identify underwater mountain ranges and trenches, as well as thousands of new marine species, forming the basis of modern oceanography. In 1914 sonar was first used to take accurate measurements.

What is the Holy Grail?

Learn all about the legendary ancient cup

Right
The bronze and iron warded lock system was used throughout the Middle Ages

The Holy Grail is a Christian legend expressed in Western European literature and art. The Grail itself is considered the most sacred Christian relic, most commonly said to be the cup from which Jesus drank at the last supper, and in which Joseph of Arimathea collected Jesus's blood at the crucifixion. Joseph of Arimathea is said to have then taken the cup to England, where it was hidden for hundreds of years. The knights of King Arthur made it their principal quest to find the cup because, according to the legend, it had special powers.

© Corbis, Wiki, Mary Evans

What did a 19th century fireman look like?

How the USA's volunteers put the fight in firefighter

D uring the late 18th century and early 19th century, firefighters in the USA didn't have such a good reputation. Firehouses were like social clubs and when news of a fire broke, the volunteers would race other fire companies to the scene. These competitions often resulted in the firefighters battling each other instead of the fire!

By the mid-19th century, insurance companies and Republican Party were lobbying for a professional fire service. When horse-drawn, steam-powered water pumps became available, volunteers were replaced with paid fire departments.

Below
Firehouses were often like social clubs, with firefighters made up of volunteers

～ Firefighters ～
Learn the anatomy of a 19th century fireman

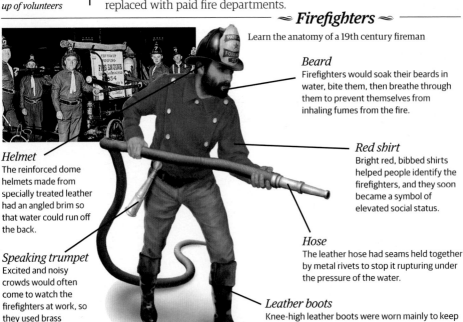

Beard
Firefighters would soak their beards in water, bite them, then breathe through them to prevent themselves from inhaling fumes from the fire.

Red shirt
Bright red, bibbed shirts helped people identify the firefighters, and they soon became a symbol of elevated social status.

Helmet
The reinforced dome helmets made from specially treated leather had an angled brim so that water could run off the back.

Hose
The leather hose had seams held together by metal rivets to stop it rupturing under the pressure of the water.

Speaking trumpet
Excited and noisy crowds would often come to watch the firefighters at work, so they used brass speaking trumpets to relay commands.

Leather boots
Knee-high leather boots were worn mainly to keep the firefighters warm and dry, rather than protect them from the flames.

Why was the Sikorsky MH-60 Black Hawk perfect for war?

A new kind of war machine, built for a new kind of battlefield

Below
The Black Hawk is capable of carrying a range of weaponry, and will often house a door gunner for protection in hostile environments

Two US companies, Boeing Vertol and Sikorsky, went head-to-head with their rival designs for the new combat helicopter, with the latter winning the contract with its S-70 prototype.

The MH-60 variant seen here was developed from the standard UH-60 Black Hawk for use during special operations. The machine's effective range was greatly increased with the addition of a more efficient fuel tank, the installation of systems for aerial refuelling, and the improvement of the craft's overall survivability. It was during a special operation that these assets would be put to the ultimate test, an incident known as Black Hawk Down.

⇝ Inside a Black Hawk ⇝

The high-powered tech behind the MH-60 military machine

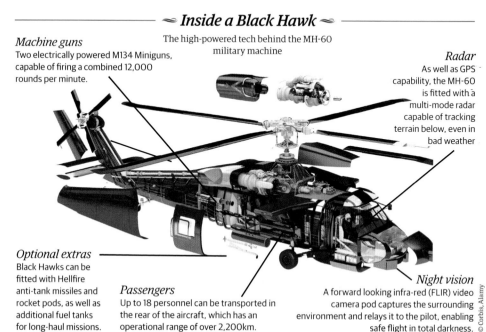

Machine guns
Two electrically powered M134 Miniguns, capable of firing a combined 12,000 rounds per minute.

Radar
As well as GPS capability, the MH-60 is fitted with a multi-mode radar capable of tracking terrain below, even in bad weather

Optional extras
Black Hawks can be fitted with Hellfire anti-tank missiles and rocket pods, as well as additional fuel tanks for long-haul missions.

Passengers
Up to 18 personnel can be transported in the rear of the aircraft, which has an operational range of over 2,200km.

Night vision
A forward looking infra-red (FLIR) video camera pod captures the surrounding environment and relays it to the pilot, enabling safe flight in total darkness.

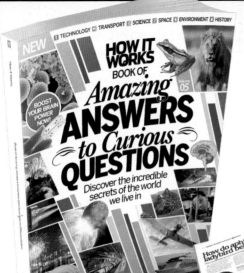